Relativity for the Million

RELATIVITY

FOR THE

MILLION

by **Martin Gardner**

Illustrated by Anthony Ravielli

THE MACMILLAN COMPANY   NEW YORK

MACMILLAN NEW YORK, LONDON

For Billie,
a relative

Second Printing, 1962

Printed in the United States of America

Library of Congress catalog card number: 62–21214

The Macmillan Company, New York
Collier-Macmillan Canada, Ltd., Galt, Ontario
Divisions of The Crowell-Collier Publishing Company

Introduction

So MANY popular books on relativity have been written that the reader may wonder: Why another one? I have three answers:

1. The best introductions to elementary relativity were written a long time ago and are now out of date. It is true that no basic changes have been made in relativity theory, but there have been new experimental confirmations, new approaches to certain problems, new cosmological models. A modern introduction should include these developments.

2. The challenge of trying to explain once more a complicated, important subject in as simple and entertaining a way as possible, without serious distortions, was a challenge hard to resist.

3. No popular book on relativity has been illustrated so elaborately. Anthony Ravielli's brilliant graphic art sets this book apart from all others.

I have resisted the temptation to add a final chapter on the philosophical consequences of relativity because I believe that, in the ordinary sense of the word "philosophical," relativity has no consequences. For the theory of knowledge and the philosophy of science it obviously has implications, chiefly through its demonstration that the mathematical structure of space and time cannot be determined without observation and experiment. But so far as the great traditional topics of philosophy are concerned—God, immortality, free will, good and evil, and so on—relativity has absolutely nothing to say. The notion that relativity physics supports the avoidance of value judgments in anthropology, for example, or a relativism with respect to morals, is absurd. Actually, relativity introduces a whole series of new "absolutes."

It is sometimes argued that relativity theory makes it more difficult to think that outside our feeble minds there is a "huge world," possessing an orderly structure that can be described in part by scientific laws. "As the subject [relativity] developed," writes the English astronomer James Jeans in his book, *The Growth of Physical Science*, "it became clear that the phenomena of nature were determined by us and our experience rather than by a mechanical universe outside us and independent of us."

This "subjectivism" or "idealism," or whatever it is called to distinguish it from the "realism" of working scientists, has in recent years been linked to relativity by several prominent physicists who ought to know better. It is a respectable enough metaphysical attitude; but it receives not the slightest support from relativity. It certainly was not Einstein's view, as you will see at once by reading the quotation that opens this book. I will not argue the point here. If the reader is interested he will find it forcibly stated by two leading contemporary philosophers of science, Adolf Grünbaum, in a paper reprinted in the anthology, *Philosophy of Science*, and Philipp Frank, in Chapter 7 of his book, *Philosophy of Science*.

I am grateful to John Stachel, Professor of Physics at the University of Pittsburgh, for reading the manuscript of this book and making valuable corrections and suggestions. Of course he cannot be held responsible for my own biases on controversial questions.

MARTIN GARDNER

Contents

OUT yonder there was this huge world, which exists independently of us human beings and which stands before us like a great, eternal riddle, at least partially accessible to our inspection and thinking. The contemplation of this world beckoned like a liberation. . . .

Albert Einstein,
Autobiographical Notes.

1

Absolute or Relative?

Two sailors, Joe and Moe, were cast away on a deserted island. Several years went by. One day Joe found a bottle that had washed ashore. It was one of those new king-size bottles of Coca-Cola. Joe turned pale.

"Hey, Moe!" he shouted. "We've shrunk!"

There is a serious lesson to be learned from this joke. The lesson is: There is no way of judging the size of an object except by comparing it with the size of something else. The Lilliputians thought Gulliver a giant. The Brobdingnagians thought Gulliver tiny. Is a billiard ball large or small? Well, it is extremely large *relative* to an atom, but extremely small *relative* to the earth.

Jules Henri Poincaré, a famous nineteenth-century French mathematician who anticipated many aspects of relativity theory, once put it in this way (scientists call his way of putting it a "thought experiment": an experiment that can be imagined but not actually performed). Suppose, he said, that during the night, while you were sound asleep, everything in the universe became a thousand times larger than before. By everything, Poincaré meant *everything:* electrons, atoms, wavelengths of light, you yourself, your bed, your house, the earth, the sun, the stars. When you awoke, would you be able to tell that anything had changed? Is there any experiment you could perform that would prove you had altered in size?

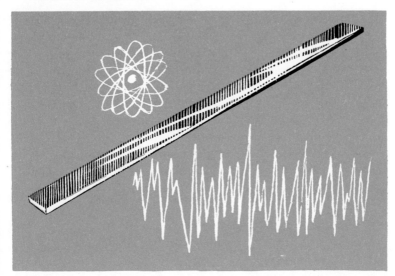

No, said Poincaré, there is no such experiment. In fact, the universe really would be the same as before. It would be meaningless even to say it had grown larger. "Larger" means larger in relation to something else. In this case there is no "something else." It would be just as meaningless, of course, to say that the entire universe had shrunk in size.

Size, then, is relative. There is no *absolute* way to measure an object and say that it is absolutely such-and-such a size. It can be measured only by applying other sizes, such as the length of a yardstick or meter rod. But how long is a meter rod? Before January 1, 1962, a meter was defined as the length of a certain platinum bar that was kept at a constant temperature in a cellar at Sèvres, France. Since January 1, 1962, the new standard for the meter is the length of 1,656,763.83 wavelengths of a certain type of orange-colored radiation given off in a vacuum by the atom of krypton 86. Of course, if everything in the universe were to grow larger or smaller in the same proportion, including the wavelength of this radiation, there would still be no experimental way to detect the change.

The same is true of periods of time. Does it take a "long" or "short" time for the earth to make one trip around the sun? To a small child, the time from one Christmas to the next seems like an eternity. To a geologist, accustomed to thinking in terms of millions of years, one year is but a fleeting instant. A period of time, like distance in space, is impossible to measure without comparing it to some other period of time. A year is measured by the earth's period of revolution around the sun; a day by the time it takes the earth to rotate once on its axis; an hour by the time it takes the long hand of a clock to make one revolution. Always one period of time is measured by comparing it with another.

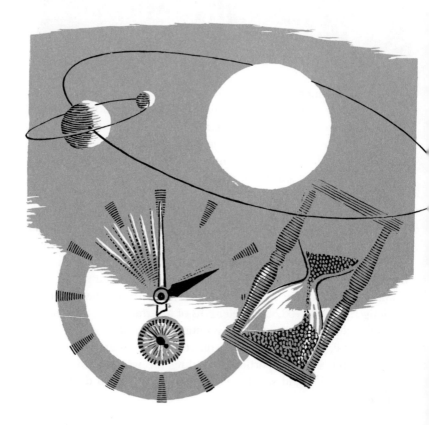

There is a famous science-fiction story by H. G. Wells called "The New Accelerator." It teaches the same lesson as the joke about the two sailors, only the lesson is about time instead of space. A scientist discovers a way to speed up all the processes of his body. His heart beats more rapidly, his brain operates faster, and so on. You can guess what happens. The world seems to slow down to a standstill. The scientist walks outside, moving slowly so the friction of the air will not set fire to his pants. The street is filled with human statues. A man is frozen in the act of winking at two passing girls. In the park, a band plays with a low-pitched, wheezy rattle. A bee buzzes through the air with the pace of a snail.

Let us try another thought experiment. Suppose that at a certain instant everything in the cosmos begins to move at a slower speed, or a faster speed, or perhaps stops entirely for a few million years, then starts up again. Would the change be perceivable? No, there is no experiment by which it could be detected. In fact, to say that such a change had occurred would be meaningless. Time, like distance in space, is relative.

Many other concepts familiar in everyday life are relative. Consider "up" and "down." In past ages it was hard for people to understand why a man on the opposite side of the earth was not hanging upside down, with all the blood rushing to his head. Children today have the same difficulty when they first learn that the earth is round. If the earth were made of transparent glass and you could look straight through it with a telescope, you would in fact see people standing upside down, their feet sticking to the glass. That is, they would appear upside down *relative to you.* Of course, *you* would appear upside down relative to *them.* On the earth "up" is the direction that is away from the center of the earth. "Down" is toward the center of the earth. In interstellar space there is no absolute up or down, because there is no planet available to serve as a "frame of reference."

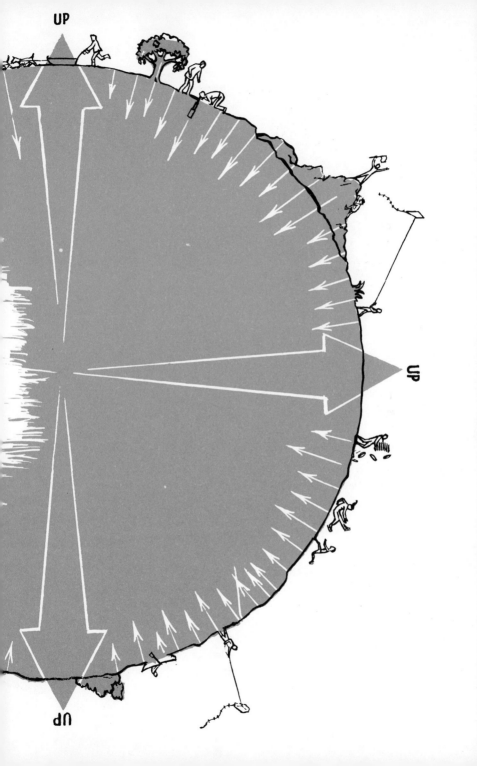

Imagine a spaceship on its way through the solar system. It is shaped like a giant doughnut and is rotating so that centrifugal force creates an artificial gravity field. Inside the ship, spacemen can walk about the outer rim of the doughnut as if it were a floor. "Down" is now *away* from the center of the ship, "up" is *toward* the center: just the opposite of how it is on a rotating planet.

So, you see there are no absolute "ups" and "downs" in the universe. Up and down are directions relative to the direction in which a gravitational field is acting. It would be meaningless to say that while you were asleep the entire cosmos turned upside down, because there is nothing to serve as a frame of reference for deciding which position the cosmos has taken.

Another type of change that is relative is the change of an object to its mirror image. If a capital R is printed in reverse form like this, Я , you recognize it immediately as the mirror image of an R. But if the entire universe (including you) suddenly became its mirror image, there would be no way that you could detect such a change. Of course, if only one person became his mirror image (H. G. Wells wrote a story about this also, "The Plattner Story") while the cosmos remained the same, then it would seem to him as if the cosmos had reversed. He would have to hold a book up to a mirror to read it, the way Alice behind the looking glass managed to read the reversed printing of "Jabberwocky" by holding the poem up to a mirror. But if *everything* reversed, there would be no experiment that could detect the change. It would be just as meaningless to say that such a reversal had occurred as it would be to say that the universe had turned upside down or doubled in size.

Is motion absolute? Is there any type of experiment that will show positively whether an object is moving or standing still? Is motion another relative concept that can be measured only by comparing one object with another? Or is there something peculiar about motion, something that makes it different from the relative concepts just considered?

Stop and think carefully about this for a while before you go on to the next chapter. It was in answer to just such questions that Einstein developed his famous theory of relativity. This theory is so revolutionary, so contrary to common sense, that even today there are thousands of scientists (including physicists) who have as much difficulty understanding its basic concepts as a child has in understanding why the people of China do not fall off the earth.

If you are young, you have a great advantage over these scientists. Your mind has not yet developed those deep furrows along which thoughts so often are forced to travel. But whatever your age, if you are willing to flex your mental muscles, there is no reason why you cannot learn to feel at home in the strange new world of relativity.

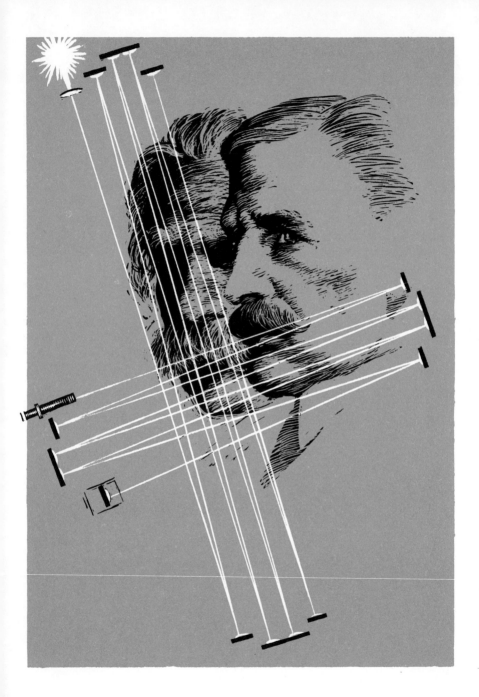

The
Michelson-Morley
Experiment

Is motion relative? After some first thoughts you may be inclined to answer, "Of course it is!" Imagine a train moving north at 60 miles per hour. On the train a man walks south at 3 miles per hour. In what direction is he moving and at what speed? It is immediately obvious that this question cannot be answered without choosing a frame of reference. Relative to the train, the man moves south at 3 miles per hour. Relative to the ground, he moves north at 60 minus 3, or 57 miles per hour.

Can we say that the man's "ground speed" (57 miles per hour) is his true, absolute speed? No, because there are other, larger frames of reference. The earth itself is moving. It both rotates and swings around the sun. The sun, with all its planets, speeds through the galaxy. The galaxy rotates and moves relative to other galaxies. The galaxies in turn form galactic clusters that move relative to each other. No one really knows how far this chain of motions can be carried. There is no apparent way to chart the absolute motion of anything; that is to say, there is no fixed, final frame of reference by which all motions can be measured. Motion and rest, like large and small, slow and fast, up and down, left and right, seem to be completely relative. There is no way to measure the motion of one object except by comparing it with the motion of some other object.

Alas, it is not so simple! If this were all there is to say about the relativity of motion, there would have been no need for Einstein to develop his theory of relativity. Physicists would have had the theory all along!

The reason it is not simple is this: there appear to be two very easy ways to detect absolute motion. One method makes use of the speed of light; the other makes use of various inertial effects that occur when a moving object alters its path or velocity. Einstein's Special Theory of Relativity deals with the first, his General Theory of Relativity with the second. In this and the next two chapters the first method that might serve as a clue to absolute motion, the method that makes use of the speed of light, will be considered.

In the nineteenth century, before the time of Einstein, physicists thought of space as containing a kind of fixed, invisible substance called the *ether*. Often it was called the "luminiferous ether," meaning that it was the bearer of light waves. It filled the entire universe. It penetrated all material substances. If all the air were pumped out of a glass bell jar, the jar would still be filled; filled with ether. Otherwise, how could light travel through the vacuum? Light is a wave motion; there had to be something there to transmit the waving. The ether itself, although it must vibrate, seldom (if ever) would move with respect to material objects; rather, all objects would move through it, like the movement of a sieve through water. The absolute motion of a star, planet, or any object whatever was (so these early physicists were convinced) simply its motion with respect to this motionless, invisible, etherial sea.

But, you may ask, if the ether is an invisible, nonmaterial substance—a substance that cannot be seen, heard, felt, smelled or tasted—how can the movement of, say, the earth ever be measured with respect to it? The answer is simple. The measurement can be

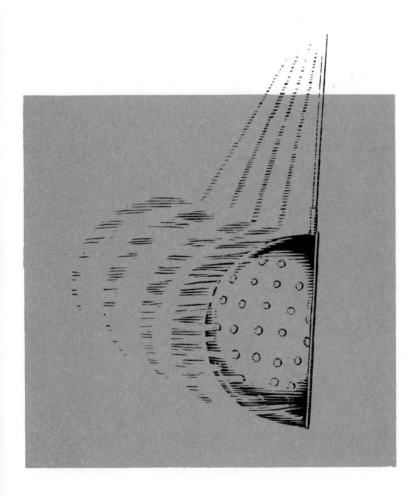

made by comparing the earth's motion with the motion of a beam of light.

To understand this, consider for a moment the nature of light. Actually, light is only the small visible portion of a spectrum of electromagnetic radiation which includes radio waves, radar waves, infrared light, ultraviolet light, and gamma rays. Everything said about light in this book applies equally to any type of electromagnetic wave, but "light" is a shorter term than "electromagnetic wave," so this term will be used throughout. Light is a wave motion. To think of such a motion without thinking also of a material ether seemed to the early physicists as preposterous as thinking about water waves without thinking of water.

If a bullet is fired straight ahead from the front of a moving jet plane, the ground speed of the bullet is faster than if it were fired from a gun held by someone on the ground. The ground speed of the bullet fired from the plane is obtained by adding the speed of the plane to the speed of the bullet. In the case of light, however, the velocity of a beam is not affected by the speed of the ob-

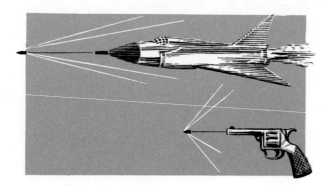

ject that sends out the beam. This was strongly indicated by experiments in the late nineteenth and early twentieth centuries, and has since been amply confirmed. The latest test was made by Russian astronomers in 1955, using light from opposite sides of the rotating sun. One edge of our sun is always moving toward us, the other edge always moving away. It was found that light from both edges travels to the earth with the same velocity. Similar tests had been made decades earlier with light from revolving double stars. Regardless of the motion of its source, the speed of light through empty space is always the same: a little more than 186,000 miles (300,000 kilometers) per second.

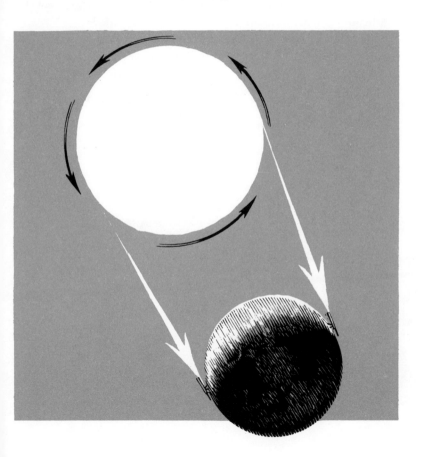

Do you see how this fact provides a means by which a scientist (we will call him the observer) could calculate his own absolute motion? If light travels through a fixed, stationary ether with a certain speed, c, and if this velocity is independent of the velocity of its source, then the speed of light can be used as a kind of yardstick for measuring the observer's absolute motion. An observer moving in the same direction as a beam of light should find the beam passing him with a speed less than c; an observer moving toward a beam of light should find the beam approaching him with a velocity greater than c. In other words, measurements of the velocity of a beam of light should vary, depending on the observer's motion relative to the beam. These variations would indicate his true, absolute motion through the ether.

Physicists often describe this situation in terms of what they call an "ether wind." To understand just what they mean by this, consider again that moving train. We have seen how the speed of a man, walking through the train at 3 miles per hour, is always the same relative to the train, regardless of whether he walks toward the engine or toward the rear of the train. The same

is true of the speed of sound waves inside a closed car. Sound is a wave motion transmitted by molecules of air. Because the air is carried along by the car, sound will travel north in the car with the same velocity (relative to the car) with which it travels south.

The situation alters if we move from the closed passenger car to an open flatcar. The air is no longer trapped inside the car. If the train moves at 60 miles per hour, there will be a wind of 60 miles per hour blowing back across the flatcar. Because of this wind, the speed of sound moving from the back to the front of the car will be less than normal. The speed of sound from front to back will be greater than normal.

Physicists of the nineteenth century believed that the ether surely must behave like the air that rushes over a moving flatcar. How could it be otherwise? If the ether is motionless, any object moving through it would have to encounter an "ether wind" blowing in the opposite direction. Light is a wave motion in this fixed ether. The velocity of light, measured on a moving object, would of course be influenced by such an ether wind.

The earth is hurtling through space, on its trip around the sun, at a speed of about 18 miles per second. This motion, the physicists reasoned, should create an ether wind of 18 miles per second, blowing past the earth and through the spaces between its atoms. To measure the absolute motion of the earth—its motion with respect to the fixed ether—all that would be necessary would be to measure the speed of light as it travels back and forth in different directions on the earth's surface. Because of the ether wind, light would surely move faster in one direction than another. By comparing the various speeds of light as it is sent in different directions, it should then be possible to calculate the absolute direction and velocity of the earth's motion at any given instant. Such an experiment was first proposed in 1875, four years before Einstein was born, by the great Scottish physicist James Clerk Maxwell.*

In 1881 Albert Abraham Michelson, then a young officer in the United States Navy, made just such an experiment. Michelson had been born in Germany, of Polish parents, but his father had taken him to America when he was two. After graduating from the U.S. Naval Academy at Annapolis and serving two years at sea, he became a teacher of physics and chemistry at the Academy.

* The suggestion appears in Maxwell's article on "Ether" in the ninth edition of *The Encyclopaedia Britannica.*

A leave of absence permitted him to study in Europe. It was at the University of Berlin, in the laboratory of the famous German physicist Hermann von Helmholtz, that young Michelson made his first attempt to detect an ether wind. To his great surprise, he could find no difference in the speed with which light traveled back and forth in any direction of the compass. It was as if a fish had discovered that it could swim in any direction through the sea without being able to detect the motion of water past its body; as if a pilot flying in the open cockpit of a plane could feel no wind against his face.

A distinguished Austrian physicist named Ernst Mach (we will hear more about him in Chapter 7) had for some time been criticizing the notion of absolute motion through the ether. He read Michelson's published report on the test and decided at once that the concept of an ether had to be discarded. However, most physicists refused to take this daring step. Michelson's apparatus had been crude. There was good reason to think that a better-designed experiment, with more sensitive equipment, would show positive results. Michelson himself thought so. He was disappointed in the "failure" of his test; eager to try again.

Michelson resigned his naval commission to become a professor of physics at the Case School of Applied Science (now the Case Institute) in Cleveland, Ohio. At nearby Western Reserve University, Edward Williams Morley was teaching chemistry. The two men became good friends. "Outwardly," writes Bernard Jaffe in his book, *Michelson and the Speed of Light*, "the two scientists were a study in contrast. . . . Michelson was good-looking and trim, always immaculately turned out. Morley, who was casual in dress, to say the least, fit the stereotype of the absent-minded

professor. . . . He let his hair grow until it curled up on his shoulders, and he wore a great bristling red mustache that straggled almost to his ears."

In 1887, in Morley's basement laboratory, the two scientists made a second, more careful attempt to detect the elusive ether wind. Their experiment, which became known as the Michelson-Morley experiment, marked one of the great turning points in modern physics.

The apparatus was mounted on a square slab of stone about five feet on the side and more than a foot thick. The slab floated on liquid mercury. This eliminated vibrations, kept the slab horizontal, and permitted it to be rotated easily around a central pin. An arrangement of mirrors on the slab sent a light beam in a certain direction; then the mirrors reflected the beam back and forth in that same direction until it had made eight round trips. (This was done to make the path as long as possible and still keep the equipment on a device that could be rotated easily.) At the same time, the mirror arrangement sent a beam of light on eight round trips in a direction at right angles to the first beam.

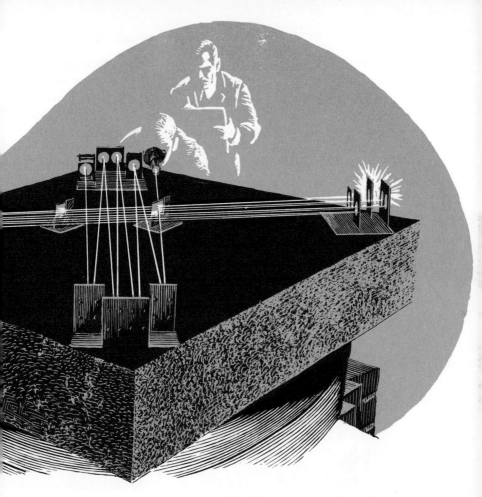

The assumption was that when the slab was turned so that one beam traveled back and forth *parallel* to the ether wind, this beam would make the trip in a longer time than it would take the other beam to go the same distance *across* the wind. At first you might think the reverse would be true. Consider the light that travels with and against the wind. Would not the wind boost the speed by the same amount one way that it would retard the speed the other way? If so, the boosts and drags would cancel each other, and the time for the total trip would be the same as if there were no wind at all.

It is true that the wind would increase the velocity of light in one direction by the same amount that it would decrease the velocity in the other direction, but—and this is the crucial point—the wind would retard the speed for a *longer period of time.* Calculation quickly shows that the entire trip would take longer than if there were no wind. The wind would also have a retarding effect on the beam that traveled across the wind at right angles. This is also easily calculated. It turns out that this retarding effect is less than in the case of the beam traveling parallel to the wind.

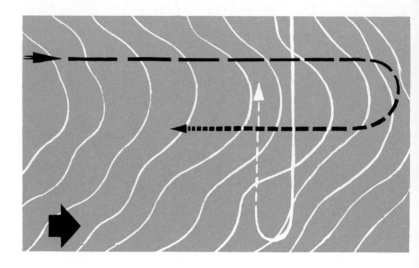

There was little doubt, then, that *if* the earth moved through an immovable sea of ether, there would be an ether wind, and if there were an ether wind, the Michelson-Morley apparatus would detect it. In fact, both scientists were confident that they would not only find such a wind, but that they could also determine (by rotating the slab until there was a maximum difference in the time it took light to make the two journeys) the exact direction, at any given moment, of the earth's path through the ether.

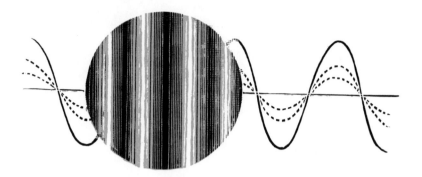

It should be pointed out that the Michelson-Morley apparatus did not measure the actual velocities of each beam of light. The two beams, after making their respective back-and-forth trips, were combined into a single beam which was viewed through a small telescope. The apparatus would then be rotated slowly. Any alteration in the relative velocities of the two beams would cause a shifting of an interference fringe pattern of alternate light and dark bands.

Again Michelson was astounded and disappointed. This time the astonishment was felt by physicists all over the world. Regardless of how Michelson and Morley turned their apparatus, they found no sign of an ether wind! Never before in the history of science had the negative results of an experiment been so positive and so shattering. Michelson once more thought his experiment a failure. He never dreamed that this "failure" would make the experiment one of the most successful, revolutionary experiments in the history of science.

Later, Michelson and Morley repeated their test with even more accurate equipment. Other physicists did the same. The most accurate test of all was made in 1960 by Charles H. Townes of Columbia University. His apparatus, using a device called a maser (an "atomic clock" based on the vibrations of molecules), was so sensitive that he could have detected an ether wind even if the earth moved at a mere one-thousandth of its actual speed. There was no trace of such a wind.

Physicists at first were so amazed by the negative results of the Michelson-Morley test that they began inventing all sorts of explanations to save the ether-wind theory. Of course, if the experiment had been performed a few centuries earlier, as G. J. Whitrow points out in his book, *The Structure and Evolution of the Universe*, a very simple explanation would immediately have occurred to everyone: The earth doesn't move! This theory seemed unlikely. The best explanation was a theory (much older than the first Michelson-Morley experiment) that the ether is dragged along by the earth, like air inside a closed train. This was Michelson's own guess. But other experiments, one by Michelson himself, ruled this out.

The strangest explanation of all was put forth by an Irish physicist, George Francis FitzGerald. Perhaps, he said, the ether wind puts pressure on a moving object, causing it to shrink a bit in the direction of motion. To determine the length of a moving object, its length at rest must be multiplied by the following simple formula, in which v^2 is the velocity of the object multiplied by itself, c^2 the velocity of light multiplied by itself:

$$\sqrt{1 - \frac{v^2}{c^2}} \, .$$

Study this formula and you will see that the amount of contraction is negligible at small velocities, increases as the velocity increases, becomes great as the object's speed approaches the speed of light. Thus, a spaceship shaped like a long cigar would, if it moved with great speed, alter its shape to that of a short cigar. The speed of light is an unobtainable limit; when this is reached the formula becomes:

$$\sqrt{1 - \frac{c^2}{c^2}} \, ,$$

which reduces to 0. Multiplying the length of the object by 0 results in 0. In other words, if an object could attain the speed of light, it would have no length at all in the direction of its motion!

FitzGerald's theory was put into elegant mathematical form by the Dutch physicist Hendrik Antoon Lorentz, who had independently thought of the same explanation. (Later, Lorentz became one of Einstein's closest friends, but at this time they did not know one another.) The theory came to be known as the Lorentz-FitzGerald (or the FitzGerald-Lorentz) contraction theory.

It is easy to understand how the contraction theory would explain the failure of the Michelson-Morley test. If the square slab and all the apparatus on it were contracted by a tiny amount in the direction in which the ether wind was blowing, the light would have a shorter total distance to travel. Even though the wind would have an over-all drag effect on the beam's back-and-forth journey, the shorter path would permit the beam to finish the trip in the same time that it would take if there were no wind and no contraction. In other words, the contraction would be just enough to keep the speed of light a constant, regardless of the direction in which the Michelson-Morley apparatus is turned.

Why, you may ask, couldn't this theory be tested simply by measuring the length of the apparatus to see if it shortens in the direction of the earth's motion? The answer is that the ruler would shorten also, in the same proportion. As a result, measurements would come out the same as if there were no contraction. The contractions would apply to *everything* on the moving earth. The

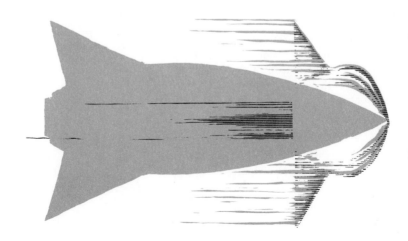

situation is similar to Poincaré's thought experiment (see Chapter 1) in which the cosmos suddenly grows a thousand times larger, except that in the Lorentz-FitzGerald theory the change would be in one direction only. Since the change applies to everything, there is no way to detect it. Within certain limits (the limits are set by topology—the study of properties that stay the same when an object is deformed), shape itself is as relative as size. The contraction of the apparatus, as well as the contraction of everything else on the earth, could be observed only by someone outside the earth and not moving with it.

Many writers on relativity have spoken of the Lorentz-Fitz-Gerald contraction hypothesis as *ad hoc*, a Latin phrase (it rhymes with *sad sock*) meaning formulated "for this case alone," and incapable of being tested by any other experiment. This is not, as Adolf Grünbaum has pointed out, strictly true. The contraction theory was *ad hoc* only in the sense that at the time there was no way to test it. In principle it is not at all *ad hoc*. In fact, it was definitely ruled out in 1932 by an important experiment called the Kennedy-Thorndike experiment.

Roy J. Kennedy and Edward M. Thorndike, two American physicists, repeated the Michelson-Morley test with this major difference: Instead of making the two arms of the apparatus as equal in length as possible, they made the lengths as different as possible. The apparatus was then rotated to see if there was any change in the difference between the times it took the two light beams to make round trips in the two directions. According to the contraction theory, this time difference would alter as the apparatus turned. It would be detected (as in Michelson's test) by changes in the interference fringes when the two beams were recombined. No such changes were observed.

An even simpler way to test the contraction theory would be to make "one-way" measurements of the speed of light; that is, to clock the speed along a straight path in the direction of the earth's motion and compare it with the speed along the same path in the opposite direction. Clearly, a contraction of the path would not make detection of an ether wind impossible, if there were an ether wind. Until the recent discovery of the Mössbauer effect (to be discussed in Chapter 8), huge technical difficulties have prevented the making of such a test. In February 1962, at a meeting of the Royal Society of London, Professor Christian Møller of the University of Copenhagen explained how such an experiment could easily be performed by using the Mössbauer effect as a source of electromagnetic radiation, mounting the source and receiver at opposite ends of a table that could be rotated. Such an experiment, Møller pointed out, would falsify the original contraction theory. By the time this book is printed, such an experiment may have been performed.

Although experiments of this sort could not be made in Lorentz's time, he realized that they could be made in principle, and there were good reasons to suppose that, like Michelson's experiment, they would show negative results. To account for such probable results, Lorentz made an important addition to his original theory. He introduced changes in time. Clocks, he said, would be slowed down by an ether wind, and in just such a way as to make the velocity of light always measure 186,000 miles per second.

For one example of how this works out, imagine that there are clocks of sufficient accuracy to make possible a "one-way" measurement of the speed of light. The light is to be sent from A to B along a straight path in the direction in which the earth is moving. Two clocks at A are synchronized, then one clock is moved to B. A note is made of the time that a light beam starts from A and the time (measured by the other clock) that the beam is received at B. Since the light would be moving *against* the ether wind, its speed should be slowed down and the time of the trip should be a little longer than it would be if the earth were at rest. Do you see the flaw in this theory? The clock, in moving from A to B, also moves against the ether wind. This slows the clock at B down a bit so that it is running slightly *behind* the clock at A. Result: The velocity of light clocks at 186,000 miles per second.

The same thing happens (Lorentz maintained) if the speed of light is measured in the reverse direction, from B to A. Two clocks are synchronized at B, then one is taken to A. A light beam is sent from B to A, moving *with* the ether wind. The beam's speed is boosted by the wind, therefore the time taken by the light beam to make the trip should be a trifle less than if the earth were at rest. However, in moving the clock from B to A, it also went with the wind. The reduction of ether-wind pressure on the moving clock allowed the clock to gain a bit in time; therefore, when the experiment is made, the clock at A is running a bit *ahead* of the clock at B. Result: The velocity of light once again clocks at 186,000 miles per second.

Lorentz's new theory not only accounted for the negative results of the Michelson-Morley experiment; it also accounted for any conceivable experiment designed to detect changes in the speed of light as a result of an ether wind. Its equations for variations in length and time were worked out in such a way that every

possible method of measuring the speed of light, from any frame of reference, would always give the same result. It is easy to understand why physicists were unhappy with this theory. It was *ad hoc* in the full sense of the word. It seemed little more than a weird effort to patch up the rents that had developed in the ether theory. There was no imaginable way either to confirm or refute it. Physicists found it hard to believe that if there were an ether wind, nature would go to such curious, drastic, almost prankish lengths to prevent it from being detected. The English philosopher-mathematician, Bertrand Russell, later described the situation aptly by quoting the following lines from Lewis Carroll's song of the White Knight in *Through the Looking-Glass:*

> But I was thinking of a plan
> To dye one's whiskers green,
> And always use so large a fan
> That they could not be seen.

Lorentz's new theory, with its time as well as length changes, seemed almost as absurd as the White Knight's plan. But try as they would, physicists were unable to think of a better plan.

The next chapter will show how Einstein's Special Theory of Relativity pointed to a bold, remarkable way out of this extraordinary confusion.

The Special
Theory of Relativity,

Part I

In 1905, when Albert Einstein published his famous paper on what later became known as the Special Theory of Relativity, he was a young married man of 26, working as an examiner for the Swiss patent office. His career as a physics student, at The Polytechnic Institute of Zürich, had not been impressive. He had preferred to read, think, and dream on his own rather than cram his mind with unessential facts in order to pass examinations with high marks. He tried teaching physics, but he was a clumsy teacher, and lost several such positions.

There is another side to this history. From the time that he was a small boy, Einstein had thought deeply about the fundamental laws of nature. He later recalled the two greatest "wonders" of his childhood: a compass his father showed him when he was four or five, and a book on Euclidian geometry that he read when he was twelve. These two "wonders" are symbolic of Einstein's life work: the compass a symbol of physical geometry, the structure of that "huge world" outside of us, about which we can never be absolutely certain; the book a symbol of pure geometry, a structure that is absolutely certain but independent of the actual world. Before he was sixteen Einstein had acquired, largely by his own efforts, a solid understanding of basic mathematics, including analytic geometry and calculus.

While Einstein was working in the Swiss patent office he was reading and thinking about all sorts of perplexing problems that had to do with light and motion. His special theory was a brilliant attempt to account for a wide variety of unexplained experiments, of which the Michelson-Morley test had been the most startling and best publicized. It is important to understand that there were many other experiments that had created a highly unsatisfactory state of affairs with respect to theory about electromagnetic phenomena. If the Michelson-Morley test had never been made, the special theory would still have been formulated. Einstein himself later spoke about the small role that it actually played in his thinking. Of course, if Michelson and Morley had detected an ether wind, the special theory would have been ruled out from the start. But the negative result of the test was only one of many things that led Einstein to his theory.

We have seen how Lorentz and FitzGerald had tried to save the ether-wind theory by assuming that the pressure of the wind, in some not-yet-understood way, causes an actual physical contraction of objects in motion. Einstein, following the footsteps of Ernst Mach, took a bolder view. The reason Michelson and Morley were unable to detect an ether wind, Einstein said, is simple: *There is no ether wind*. He did not say that there is no ether; only that the ether, if it exists, is of no value in measuring uniform motion. (In recent years a number of prominent physicists have proposed that the term "ether" be restored, though not, of course, in the old sense of an immovable frame of reference.)

Classical physics—the physics of Isaac Newton—made clear that if you are on a uniformly moving object, say a train car that is closed on all sides so you cannot see the scenery go by, there is no mechanical experiment by which you can prove that you are moving. (This assumes, of course, that the uniform motion is completely smooth, with no bumps or swaying of the car that can serve as clues to motion.) If you toss a ball straight up in the air, it comes straight down again. This is exactly what would happen if the train were standing still. An observer on the ground outside the moving car, if he could see through the sides of the car, would see the ball's path as a curve. But to you inside the car, the ball goes straight up and down. It is fortunate that objects behave in this way. Otherwise, one could never play a game like tennis or baseball. Each time the ball went up in the air, the earth would move out from under it at 18 miles per second!

The Special Theory of Relativity carries the classical relativity of Newton forward another step. It says that in addition to being unable to detect the train's motion by a *mechanical* experiment, it also is impossible to detect its motion by an *optical* experiment; more precisely, by an experiment with electromagnetic radiation. The special theory can be put in a nutshell: It is not possible to measure uniform motion in any absolute way. If we are on a smoothly, uniformly moving train, we have to peek through a window and look at some other object, say a telephone pole, to make sure we are moving. Even then we cannot say positively whether the train is moving past the pole or the pole moving past the train. The best we can do is say that the train and the ground are in relative uniform motion.

Note the constant repetition in the last paragraph of that word "uniform." Uniform motion is motion in a straight line at a constant speed. Nonuniform or *accelerated* motion is motion that is getting faster or slower (when it is getting slower the acceleration is said to be negative), or motion along a path that is not a straight line. The Special Theory of Relativity has nothing new to say about accelerated motion.

The relativity of uniform motion seems harmless enough, but the fact is that it plunges us immediately into a strange new world that at first seems to resemble nothing so much as the nonsense world behind Lewis Carroll's looking-glass. For if there is no way to measure uniform motion relative to a universal, fixed frame

of reference like the ether, then light must behave in an utterly fantastic way, completely contrary to all experience.

Consider an astronaut in a spaceship that is racing alongside a light beam. The ship is traveling with half the speed of light. The astronaut will find, if he makes the proper measurements, that the beam is still passing him at its usual velocity of 186,000 miles per second! Think about this for a moment and you will soon realize that this must indeed be the case if the notion of an ether wind is discarded. If the astronaut found that light slowed down relative to his motion, he would have detected the very ether wind that Michelson and Morley failed to detect. Similarly, if his spaceship travels directly toward a source of light, moving with half of light's speed, will he find the beam approaching him twice as fast? No, it is still moving toward him at 186,000 miles per second. Regardless of how he moves relative to the beam, his measurements will always give the beam the same speed.

Frequently one hears the remark that relativity theory makes everything in physics relative, that it destroys all absolutes. Nothing could be further from the truth. It makes some things relative that were previously thought absolute, but in doing so it introduces new absolutes. In classical physics the speed of light was relative in the sense that it should appear to change depending on the motion of the observer. In the Special Theory of Relativity, the speed of light becomes, in this sense, a new absolute. No matter how a source of light moves, or how an observer moves, the speed of light relative to the observer never changes.

Imagine two spaceships A and B. There is nothing in the cosmos except these two ships. They move toward each other at uniform speed. Is there any way that astronauts on either ship can decide which of the following three situations is "true" or "absolute"?

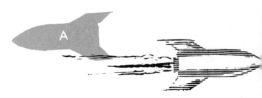

1. Spaceship A is at rest, B is moving.

2. Spaceship B is at rest, A is moving.

3. Both ships are moving.

Einstein's answer is: No, there is no way to decide. An astronaut on either ship can, if he wishes, choose to make ship A the fixed frame of reference. There is no experiment of any sort, including experiments with light or any other electrical or magnetic phenomena, that will prove this choice wrong. The same is true if he chooses to make ship B the frame of reference. If he prefers to regard both ships as moving, he simply chooses a frame of reference outside the two ships; a spot relative to which both ships are in motion. There is no question of one of these choices being "right" and the others "wrong." To speak of an absolute motion of either ship is to say something that has no meaning. There is only one reality: a relative motion that brings the ships closer together at uniform speed.

In a book of this sort it is impossible to go into technical details about the special theory, especially details that involve its mathematics. We must be content with mentioning some of the more surprising consequences that follow logically from what Einstein calls the two "fundamental postulates" of his theory:

1. There is no way to tell whether an object is at rest or in uniform motion relative to a fixed ether.

2. Regardless of the motion of its source, light always moves through empty space with the same constant speed.

(The second postulate should not be confused, as it so often is, with the constant speed of light relative to a uniformly moving *observer*. This is a *deduction* from the postulates.)

Other physicists had, of course, considered these two postulates. Lorentz had tried to reconcile them by his theory in which absolute lengths and times were altered by the pressure of the ether wind. Most physicists thought this too radical a violation of common sense. They preferred to believe that the postulates were incompatible and at least one of them must be wrong. Einstein thought about the problem more deeply. The postulates were incompatible, he said, only if one refused to give up the classical view that length and time were absolute. When Einstein published his theory, he did not know that Lorentz had been thinking along similar lines, but like Lorentz, he recognized that measurements of length and time must depend on the relative motion of object and observer. Lorentz, however, had gone only halfway. He had kept the notion of an absolute length and time for objects at rest. He thought that the ether wind distorted "true" length and time. Einstein went the full way. There is, he said, no ether wind. There is no meaning to the concepts of absolute length and time. This is the key to Einstein's special theory. When he turned it, all sorts of locks began slowly to open.

To explain his special theory in a nontechnical way, Einstein once introduced the following famous thought experiment. Imagine, he said, an observer M who is standing beside a railroad track. At a certain distance down the track is a spot A. At the same distance up the track is a spot called B. Lightning happens to strike simultaneously at points A and B. The observer knows these events are simultaneous, because he sees the two flashes at the same instant. Since he is midway between them, and since light travels at a constant speed, he calculates that the lightning struck simultaneously in the two spots.

Now assume that when the lightning strikes, a train is moving at great speed along the track in the direction from A to B. At the instant the two flashes occur, an observer on the train—we call him M′—is exactly opposite observer M on the track. Since M′ is moving toward one flash and away from the other, he will see the flash at B before he sees the flash at A. Knowing that he is in motion, he will make allowances for the speed of light; he too will calculate that the two flashes occurred simultaneously.

All well and good. But, according to the two fundamental postulates of the special theory (and confirmed by the Michelson-Morley test), we have just as much right to assume that the train is at rest while the ground moves rapidly backward under the train's wheels. From *this* point of view, M', the observer on the train, will conclude that the flash at B actually did occur ahead of the flash at A, just as he observed them. He knows that he is midway between the two flashes and, since he regards himself as at rest, he is forced to conclude that the flash he saw first must have occurred before the flash he saw second.

M, the observer on the ground, is forced to agree. True, he sees the flashes as simultaneous, but now *he* is the one who is assumed to be moving. When he makes allowances for the speed of light and the fact that he is moving toward the flash at A and away from the flash at B, he will calculate that the flash at B must have taken place first.

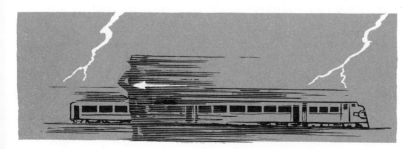

We are driven to conclude, therefore, that the question of whether the flashes are simultaneous cannot be answered in any absolute way. The answer depends on the choice of a frame of reference. Of course, if two events occur simultaneously *at the same spot,* it can be said absolutely that they are simultaneous. When two airplanes collide in midair, there is no frame of reference from which the smashing of both planes will not be simultaneous. But the greater the distance between two events, the greater the difficulty of deciding about simultaneity. It is important to understand that this is not just a question of being unable to learn the truth of the matter. *There is no actual truth of the matter.* There is no absolute time throughout the universe by which absolute simultaneity can be measured. Absolute simultaneity of distant events is a meaningless concept.

How radical this notion is can be seen by a thought experiment in which vast distances and enormous speeds are involved. Suppose that someone on Planet X, in another part of our galaxy, is trying to communicate with the earth. He sends out a radio message. This is, of course, an electromagnetic wave that travels through space with the speed of light. Assume that the earth and Planet X are 10 light-years apart, which means that it takes 10 years for the message to travel to the earth. Twelve years before a radio astronomer on earth receives the message, the astronomer had received a Nobel Prize. The special theory permits us to say, without qualification, that he received this prize *before* the message was sent from Planet X.

Ten minutes after receiving the message, the astronomer sneezes. The special theory also permits us to say, without qualification, and for all observers in any frame of reference, that the astronomer sneezed *after* the message was sent from Planet X

Now suppose that some time during the 10-year period, while the radio message was on its way to the earth (say, 3 years before the message was received), the astronomer fell off his radio telescope and broke a leg. The special theory does *not* permit us to say without qualification that he broke his leg before or after the sending of the message from Planet X.

The reason is this. One observer, leaving Planet X at the time the message is sent and traveling to the earth with a speed judged from the earth to be slow, will find (according to his measurements of the passing of time) that the astronomer broke his leg *after* the message was sent. Of course he will arrive on earth long after the message is received, perhaps centuries after. But when he calculates the date on which the message was sent, according to his clock, it will be earlier than the date on which the astronomer broke his leg. On the other hand, another observer, who also leaves Planet X at the time the message is sent, but who travels very close to the speed of light, will find that the astronomer broke his leg *before* the message was sent. Instead of taking centuries to make the trip, he will make it in, say, only a trifle more than 10 years as calculated on the earth. But because of the slowing down of time on the fast-moving spaceship, it will seem to the ship's astronaut that he made the trip in only a few months. He will be told on the earth that the astronomer broke his leg a little more than 3 years ago. According to the astronaut's clock, the message was sent a few months ago. He will conclude that the leg was broken years before the message left Planet X.

If the astronaut traveled as fast as light (of course this is purely hypothetical; not possible in fact), his clock would stop completely. It would seem to him that he made the trip in zero time. From his point of view the two events, the sending of the message and its reception, would be simultaneous. *All* events on earth during the 10-year period would appear to him to have occurred before the message was sent. Now, according to the special theory there is no "preferred" frame of reference: no reason to prefer the point of view of one observer rather than another. The calculations made by the fast-moving astronaut are just as legitimate, just as "true," as the calculations made by the slow-moving astronaut. There is no universal, absolute time that can be appealed to for settling the differences between them.

This breakdown in the classical notion of absolute simultaneity is by all odds the most "beautifully unexpected" aspect of the special theory. (The phrase "beautifully unexpected" is borrowed from a recent speech on relativity by the nuclear physicist Edward Teller.) Newton took for granted that one universal time permeated the entire cosmos. So did Lorentz and Poincaré. It was *this* that prevented them from discovering the special theory ahead of Einstein! Einstein had the genius to see that the theory could not be formulated in a comprehensive, logically consistent way without giving up completely the notion of a universal cosmic time.

There are, said Einstein, only local times. On the earth, for example, everyone is being carried along through space at the same speed; therefore, their watches all run on the same "earth time." A local time of this sort, for a moving object like the earth, is called that object's "proper time." There is still an absolute "before" and "after" (obviously no astronaut is going to die before he is born), but when events are separated by vast distances, there are long time intervals within which it is not possible to say which of two events is before or after the other. The answer depends on the observer's motion with respect to the two events. Of course the decision reached by one observer is just as "true" as a different decision reached by another observer. All this follows with iron logic from the two fundamental postulates of the special theory.

When the concept of simultaneity falls, other concepts fall with it. Time becomes relative, of course, because observers differ in their estimates of the time that elapses between the same two events. Length also becomes relative. The length of a moving train cannot be measured without knowing exactly where the front and back ends are *at the same instant.* If someone reports that at 1:00 o'clock the front end of a train was exactly opposite him and that the back end was a mile down the track at some time between 12:59 and 1:01, there obviously is no way of determining the exact length of the train. In other words, a method of establishing exact simultaneity is essential for the accurate measurements of distances and the lengths of moving objects. In the absence of such a method, the lengths of moving objects become dependent on the choice of a frame of reference.

For example, if two spaceships are in relative motion, an ob-

server on each ship will measure the other ship as contracted slightly in the direction of its motion. At ordinary speeds this change is extremely minute. The earth, which moves at 18 miles per second around the sun, would appear, to an observer at rest relative to the sun, as shortened only by a few inches. When relative speeds are very great, however, the change becomes significant. It turned out, happily, that the same formula for contraction that had been devised by FitzGerald and Lorentz, to explain the Michelson-Morley test, could be applied here. In relativity theory it is still called the Lorentz-FitzGerald contraction, but it would be less confusing if it had some other name, because Einstein gave the formula a fundamentally different interpretation.

For Lorentz and FitzGerald the contraction was a physical change, caused by pressure of the ether wind. For Einstein it had only to do with the results of measurement: in this case, when the astronauts on one spaceship measure the length of the other ship. The observers on each ship detect no change in the length of their own ship, or the lengths of objects inside it. When they

measure the other ship, however, they find it shorter. Lorentz and FitzGerald still thought of moving objects as having absolute "rest lengths." When objects contracted, they were no longer their "true" lengths. Einstein, by giving up the ether, made the concept of absolute length meaningless. What remained was *length as measured,* and this turned out to vary with the relative speed of object and observer.

How is it possible, you ask, for each ship to be shorter than the other? You ask an improper question. The theory does not say that each ship is shorter than the other. It says that astronauts on each ship *measure* the other ship as shorter. This is a quite different matter. If two people stand on opposite sides of a huge concave lens, each sees the other as smaller; but that is not the same as saying that each *is* smaller.

In addition to apparent changes in length, there also are apparent changes in time. Astronauts on each ship will find that clocks on the other ship are running slower. A simple thought experiment shows that this must indeed be the case. Imagine that you are looking out through the porthole of one spaceship into the porthole of another ship. The two ships are passing each other with a uniform speed close to that of light. As they pass, a beam of light on the other ship is sent from its ceiling to its floor. There it strikes a mirror and is reflected back to the ceiling again. You will see the path of this light as a V. If you had sufficiently accurate instruments (of course no such instruments exist) you could clock the time it takes this light beam to traverse the V-shaped path. By dividing the length of the path by the time, you obtain the speed of light.

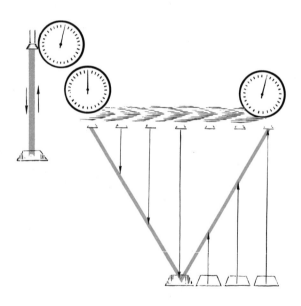

Now suppose that while you clock the light beam on its V-shaped path, an astronaut inside the other ship is doing the same thing. From his point of view, assuming *his* ship to be the fixed frame of reference, the light simply goes down and up along the same line, obviously a shorter distance than along the V that you observed. When he divides this distance by the time it took the beam to go down and up, he also obtains the speed of light. Because the speed of light is constant for all observers, he must get exactly the same final result that you did: 186,000 miles per second. But his light path is shorter. How can his result be the same? There is only one possible explanation: His clock is slower. Of course, the situation is perfectly symmetrical. If you send a beam down and up inside your ship, he will see its path as V-shaped. He will deduce that *your* clock is slower.

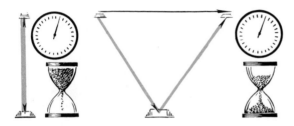

The fact that these bewildering changes of length and time are called "apparent" does not mean that there is a "true" length or time which merely "appears" different to different observers. Length and time are relative concepts. They have no meaning apart from the relation of an object to an observer. There is no question of one set of measurements being "true," another set "false." Each is true relative to the observer making the measurements; relative to his frame of reference. *There is no way that measurements can be any truer.* In no sense are they optical illusions, to be explained by a psychologist. They can be recorded on instruments. They do not require a *living* observer.

Mass too is a relative concept, but we must defer this and other matters to the next chapter.

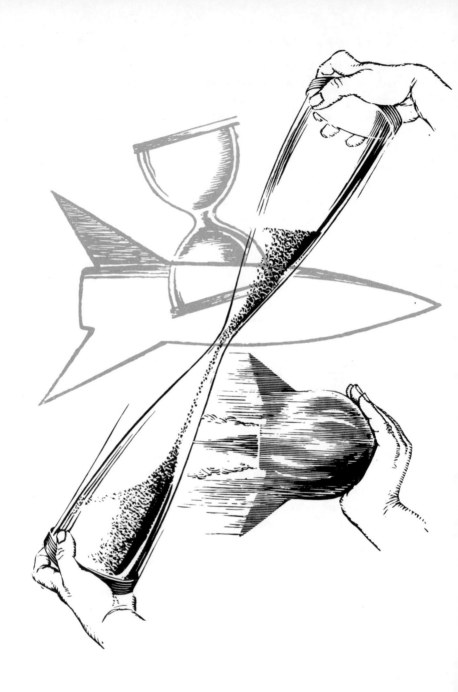

The Special
Theory of Relativity,

Part II

LENGTH and time, as was shown in the previous chapter, are relative concepts. If two spaceships pass each other with uniform velocity, observers on each ship will find that astronauts on the other ship are thinner and moving about more slowly. If the relative speed is great enough, they will seem to move like actors in a slow-motion picture. All phenomena with periodic movements will seem reduced in speed: tuning forks, balance-wheel watches, heartbeats, vibrating atoms, and so on. As Arthur Stanley Eddington, a distinguished English astronomer who had become one of Einstein's earliest, most ardent converts, once expressed it, even cigars on the other ship will seem to last longer. A six-foot astronaut, standing erect in a horizontally moving ship, will still appear six feet tall, but his body will seem thinner in the line of travel. When he lies down with his body in line with the ship's motion, his body will be restored to normal width but he will now seem shorter from head to toes.

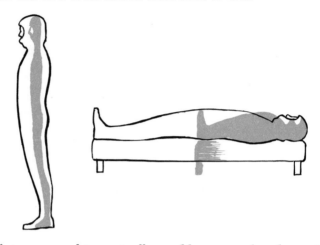

If two spaceships actually could pass each other with a relative speed great enough to make such changes significant, all sorts of technical difficulties would make it virtually impossible for observers on either ship to *see* such changes. Writers like to explain relativity by using oversimplified dramatic illustrations. These colorful illustrations do not describe changes that actually could be observed, either by the human eye or by any instruments presently known. They should be thought of as changes that could, in principle, be inferred by the astronauts on the basis of measurements with sufficiently precise instruments, and after making necessary corrections for the velocity of light.

In addition to changes in length and time, there also are relativistic changes in mass. Mass, in a rough sense, is a measure of the amount of matter in an object. A lead ball and a cork ball may be the same size, but the lead ball is more massive. It contains a greater concentration of matter.

There are two ways to measure an object's mass. It can be

weighed or it can be determined how much force is needed to accelerate the object by a certain amount. The first method is not a very good one, because the results vary with the local strength of gravity. A lead ball, carried to the top of a high mountain, will weigh a trifle less than before, although its mass remains exactly the same. On the moon its weight would be considerably less than on the earth. On Jupiter its weight would be considerably more.

The second method of measuring mass gives the same result regardless of whether one is on the earth, the moon, or Jupiter; but it is subject to a different and odder kind of variation. To determine the mass of a moving object by this method, one must measure the force required to accelerate it by a certain amount. Clearly, a stronger push is needed to start a cannonball rolling than to start a cork ball rolling. Mass measured in this way is called *inertial mass* to distinguish it from *gravitational mass* or weight. Such measurements cannot be made without making measurements of time and distance. The inertial mass of a cannonball, for example, is expressed by the amount of force required to increase its speed (distance per unit time) by so much per unit of time. As we have seen, time and distance measurements vary with the relative speed of object and observer. As a result, measurements of inertial mass also vary.

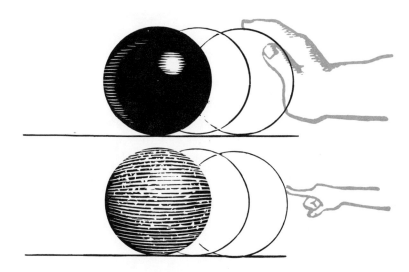

In Chapter 6 we will return to the concept of gravitational mass and its relation to inertial mass. Here we are concerned only with inertial mass as measured by an observer. For observers at rest relative to an object—for example, astronauts carrying an elephant on a spaceship—the object's inertial mass remains the same regardless of the speed with which the ship is traveling. The elephant's mass, as measured by such observers, is called its *proper mass* or *rest mass*. The same elephant's inertial mass, measured by an observer in relative motion with the elephant (for example, by an observer on the earth) is called the elephant's *relativistic mass*. The rest mass of an object never varies. Its relativistic mass does. Both are measurements of inertial mass. In this chapter we are concerned only with inertial mass; when the word "mass" is used it should always be taken in that sense.

All three variables—length, time, mass—are covered by the same Lorentz contraction formula given on Page 26. Length and the speed of clocks vary in the same direct proportion, so the formula is the same for each. Mass and the length of time intervals vary in inverse proportion, which means that the formula has to be written like this:

$$\frac{1}{\sqrt{1 - \dfrac{v^2}{c^2}}} \, .$$

The mass of an object, measured by an observer in uniform motion relative to the object, is obtained by multiplying the object's rest mass by the above formula (where v is the relative velocity of the object, c the speed of light).

For example, if the relative speed of two spaceships is 161,000 miles per second, observers on either ship will find the other ship half as long, its clocks running half as fast, its hours twice as long, and its mass twice as large. Of course, the astronauts will find everything completely normal inside their own ship. If the ships could attain a relative speed equal to that of light, observers on each ship would think the other ship had shrunk to zero in length,

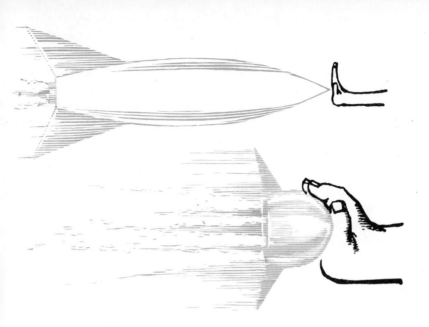

acquired an infinite mass, and that time on the other ship had slowed to a full stop!

If inertial mass did not vary in this way, then the steady application of force, such as the force supplied by rocket motors, could keep increasing a ship's velocity until it passed the speed of light. This cannot occur, because as the ship goes faster and faster (from the standpoint, say, of an observer on the earth), its relativistic mass keeps increasing in the same proportion as its length and time are decreasing. When the ship has contracted to one-tenth its rest length, its relativistic mass has become ten times as great. It is offering ten times as much resistance to its rocket motors; therefore, ten times as much force is required to produce the same increase in speed as would be required if the ship were at rest. The speed of light can never be reached. If it were reached, the outside observer would find that the ship had shrunk to zero length, had acquired an infinite mass, and was exerting an infinite force with its rocket motors. Astronauts inside the ship would observe no changes in themselves, but they would find the cosmos hurtling backward with the speed of light, cosmic time at a standstill, every star flattened to a disk and infinitely massive.

Only a science-fiction writer would dare speculate on what astronauts might observe from a ship moving faster than light. Perhaps the cosmos would appear to turn inside out and become its own mirror image, stars would acquire negative mass, and cosmic time would run backward. I hasten to add that none of this follows from the formulas of the special theory. If the speed of light is exceeded, the formulas give values to length, time, and mass that are what mathematicians call "imaginary numbers": numbers that involve the square root of minus one. Who can say? Maybe a ship that broke the light barrier would plunge straight into the Land of Oz!

After learning that nothing can outrun light, beginning students of relativity are often perplexed when they come across references to velocities faster than light. To understand exactly what relativity has to say on this point, it will be best to introduce the term "inertial frame." (Earlier writers on relativity called it "inertial system" or "Galilean system.") When an object like a spaceship is in uniform motion, that object and all objects moving along with it in the same direction and with the same speed (such as all the objects inside the ship), are said to be attached to the same inertial frame. (To be more technical, the inertial frame is the Cartesian coordinate system to which the spaceship is attached.) Outside the context of a specific inertial frame, the special theory no longer applies and there are many ways that speeds faster than light can be observed.

Consider, for example, this simple situation. A spaceship, traveling at three-fourths the speed of light, passes overhead going due east. At the same instant another spaceship, also traveling at three-fourths the speed of light, passes overhead going due west. From your frame of reference, attached to the inertial frame of the earth, the two ships pass each other with a relative velocity of one and one-half times the speed of light. They approach at that speed, move apart at that speed. There is nothing in relativity theory to deny this. However, the special theory does insist that *if you were riding on either ship*, you would calculate the relative speed of the ships to be less than that of light.

In this book we are trying our best to avoid the mathematics of relativity, but like the Lorentz contraction formula, the formula below is too simple to leave out. If x is the speed of one ship relative to the earth and y is the speed of the other ship relative to the earth, then the speed of the ships relative to each other, *as seen from the earth*, is, of course, x plus y. But as seen by an observer on either ship, we have to add velocities by the following formula:

$$\frac{x+y}{1+\frac{xy}{c^2}}.$$

In this formula c is the velocity of light. It is easy to see that when the speeds of the ships are small compared to light, the formula gives a result that is almost the same as the result obtained by adding the two velocities in the usual manner. But if the speeds of the ships are very great, the formula gives a quite different result. Take the limiting case and assume that instead of spaceships there are two beams of light passing overhead in opposite directions. The earth observer sees them separate with a speed of $2c$, or twice the speed of light. But if he were riding on one beam, he would calculate this speed, according to the formula, as

$$\frac{c + c}{1 + \dfrac{c^2}{c^2}},$$

which, of course, reduces to the value of c. In other words, he would see the other beam moving away from him with the speed of light.

Suppose that a beam of light passes overhead at the same time that a spaceship moves in the opposite direction with a speed of x. From the earth's inertial frame, ship and light pass each other with a speed of c plus x. The reader may enjoy using the formula to calculate the speed of light as observed from the spaceship's inertial frame. It turns out, of course, to be c again.

Outside the province of the special theory, which is concerned only with inertial frames, it is still possible to speak of the speed of light as an absolute limit. But now it has to be phrased in a different way: There is no way to send a *signal*, from one material body to another, with a speed faster than light. "Signal" is here used in a wide sense to include any sort of cause-and-effect chain by which a message can be transmitted: the sending of a physical object, for instance, or the transmission of any type of energy such as a sound wave, electromagnetic wave, shock wave in a solid, and so on. A message cannot be sent to Mars with a speed greater than the speed of light. This cannot be done by writing a letter and sending it in a rocket, because as we have seen, the rocket's relative speed must always be less than the speed of light. If the message is coded and sent by radio or radar, it goes *at* the speed of light. No other type of energy can provide a faster transmission of the code.

Although signals cannot be sent faster than the speed of light, it is possible to observe certain types of motion that, relative to the observer, will have a speed faster than light. Imagine a gigantic pair of scissors, the blades as long as from here to the planet Neptune. The scissors begin to close with uniform speed. As this happens, the point where the cutting edges intersect will move toward the points of the scissors with greater and greater velocity. Imagine yourself sitting on the motionless pin that joins the blades. Relative to your inertial frame, the point of intersection of the blades will soon be moving away from you with a speed greater than that of light. Of course, it is not a material object that is moving, but a geometrical point.

Perhaps this thought occurs to you: Suppose that the handles of the scissors are on the earth and the point of intersection of the blades is at Neptune. As you wiggle the handles slightly, the intersection point jiggles back and forth. Could you not, then, trans-

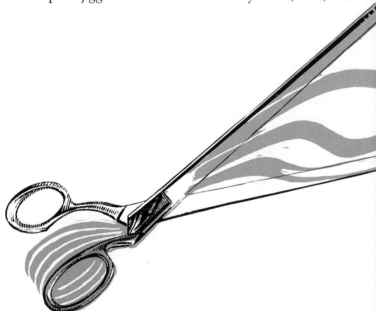

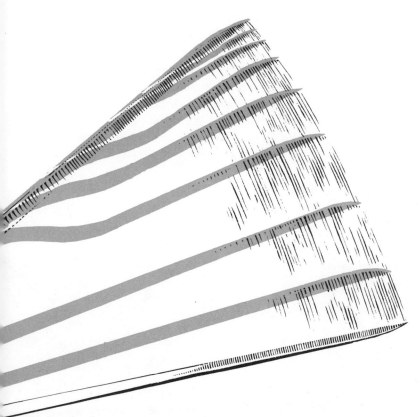

mit signals almost instantaneously to Neptune? No, because the impulse that moves the blades has to pass from molecule to molecule, and this transmission must be slower than light. There are no absolutely rigid bodies in general relativity. Otherwise you could simply extend a rigid rod from the earth to Neptune and send messages instantaneously by wiggling one end. There is no way that the giant pair of scissors, or any other type of so-called rigid object, could be used for transmitting a signal with a speed faster than the speed of light.

If a searchlight beam is aimed at a screen that is big enough and far enough away, the searchlight can be turned to make the spot on the screen move across the screen faster than light. Here again, no material object is moving. The motion is really an illusion. If the searchlight is aimed out in space and rotated, distant parts of the beam will sweep through space at a speed far beyond that of light. Chapter 5 will show that it is permissible to assume that the earth is a nonrotating frame of reference. From this point of view, the stars will have a circular velocity around the earth that is much greater than the speed of light. As one cosmologist has pointed out, a star only 10 light-years away has a relative velocity around the earth of twenty thousand times the speed of light. It is not necessary even to look to the stars for this geometrical method of breaking the light barrier. By spinning a top, a child can give the moon a rotational speed (relative to a coordinate system attached to the top) that is far in excess of 186,000 miles per second.

Chapter 10 explains that, according to one popular theory about the universe, distant galaxies may be moving away from the earth with a velocity greater than that of light. None of these examples contradicts the assertion that the speed of light is a barrier to sending signals from one material body to another.

An important consequence of the special theory, which can be touched upon only briefly, is that under certain conditions energy will change to mass and under certain other conditions mass will change to energy. Physicists used to think that the total amount of mass in the cosmos never changes and the total amount of energy never changes. This was expressed by the laws of the "conservation of mass" and the "conservation of energy." Now the two laws have merged into one single law, the "conservation of mass-energy."

When rocket motors accelerate a spaceship, part of the energy goes into the ship's increased relativistic mass. When energy is put into a coffeepot by heating—that is, by speeding up its molecules —the pot actually weighs a trifle more than it did before. As the coffee cools, mass is lost. When a watch is energized by winding, it actually gains a tiny amount of mass. As the watch runs down, it loses the mass. Such gains and losses of mass are so infinitesimal that they would never be considered in the ordinary calculations of physics. The change from mass to energy is not so infinitesimal, however, when a hydrogen bomb explodes!

The bomb's explosion is the sudden conversion to energy of part of the mass of the bomb's material. Energy radiated by the sun has a similar origin. The sun's enormous gravity puts the hydrogen gas in its interior under such great pressure, raises the gas to such a high temperature, that hydrogen is fused, or converted, into helium. In this process some mass is turned into energy. The equation that expresses the relation of mass to energy is, as everyone now knows:

$$e = mc^2,$$

where e is energy, m is mass, and c^2 is the velocity of light multiplied by itself. This equation was formulated by Einstein in con-

nection with his special theory. It is easy to see from the formula that an exceedingly small bit of mass is capable of releasing a monstrous amount of energy. Life on earth would not exist without the sun's energy, so in a sense life depends on this formula. Now it appears as if the end of life on earth is also bound up with the formula. It is no exaggeration to say that learning how to cope with the terrible fact expressed by this simple equation is the greatest problem that has ever faced mankind.

The bomb, however, is only the most spectacular of many confirmations of the special theory. Experimental evidence began to accumulate almost as soon as the ink was dry on Einstein's 1905 paper. It is, in fact, one of the best-confirmed theories of modern physics. It is confirmed every day in the laboratories of atomic scientists who work with particles that travel with a speed close to that of light. The faster such particles move, the greater the force needed to accelerate them by a given amount: in other words, the greater their relativistic mass. This is precisely why physicists keep building larger and larger machines for accelerating particles. They need stronger and stronger fields to overcome the increasing mass of particles as they are boosted closer and closer to the speed of light. Electrons can now be accelerated to 0.999999999 + the speed of light. This gives to each electron a mass (relative to the earth's inertial frame) that is about forty thousand times its mass at rest!

When a particle collides with its antiparticle (a particle of the same structure but opposite electrical charge), there is total and mutual annihilation. The entire mass of both particles turns into radiant energy. So far, this has been done in the laboratory only with individual, short-lived particles. If physicists ever succeed in constructing antimatter (matter made up of antiparticles) they will be able to achieve the ultimate in atomic power. A tiny amount of antimatter on a spaceship, kept suspended by magnetic fields, could be combined slowly with matter to provide propulsion sufficient to carry the ship to the stars.

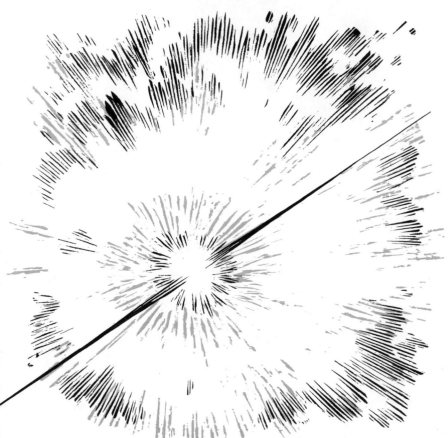

So thoroughly has the Special Theory of Relativity been confirmed by experiment that it would be hard to find a physicist today who doubts the theory's essential soundness.

Uniform motion is relative. But before it can be said that *all*
motion is relative, there is one last hurdle to cross: the hurdle of
inertia. Exactly what this hurdle is and how Einstein crossed it
will be the topic of Chapter 5.

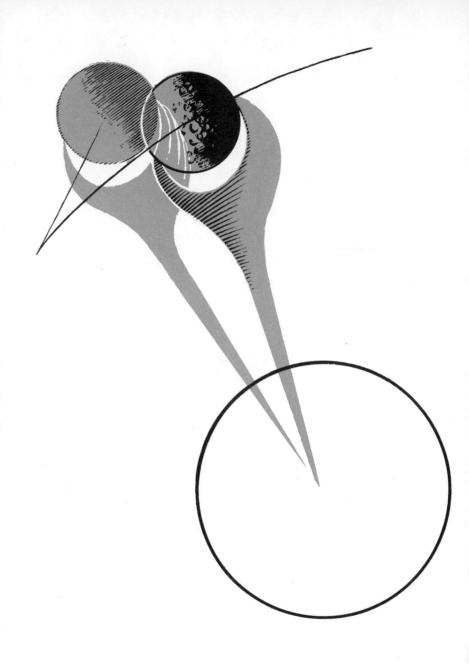

The General
Theory of
Relativity

AT the beginning of the second chapter it was pointed out that there are two ways by which absolute motion might be detected: by measuring motion with respect to a beam of light, and by making use of inertial effects that arise when an object is accelerated. The first method was shown by the Michelson-Morley experiment to be unworkable. Einstein's Special Theory of Relativity explained why. This chapter turns to the second method: the use of inertial effects as clues to absolute motion.

When a rocket ship blasts off, an astronaut inside the ship is

pressed against the back of his seat with enormous force. This is
a familiar inertial effect caused by the rocket's acceleration. Does
not this indicate that it is the rocket that is moving? In order to
maintain that all motion is relative, including accelerated motion,
it must be possible to choose the rocket as a fixed frame of reference. In such a case, the earth and the entire cosmos must be regarded as moving backward, away from the rocket. But if the
situation is viewed in this way, how can the inertial forces that act
on the astronaut be explained? The force with which he is pressed
against his seat seems to indicate, beyond any doubt, that the
rocket moves, not the cosmos.

Another convenient example is provided by the rotating earth.

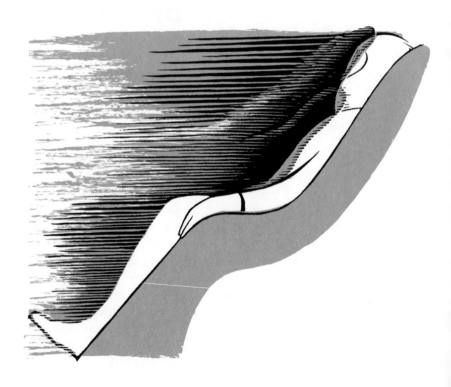

Centrifugal force, an inertial effect that accompanies rotation, causes the earth to bulge slightly at the equator. If all motion is relative, does it not follow that the earth can be chosen as a fixed frame of reference, with the cosmos rotating around it? This can certainly be imagined, but then what would cause the earth's equator to bulge? The bulge seems to indicate that it is the earth, not the universe, that rotates. Incidentally, astronomers are not agreed as to whether centrifugal force continues to maintain the equatorial bulge, or whether the bulge developed in past geologic ages when the earth was more plastic, and has now become a feature of a rigid earth, a feature that would remain even if the earth stopped rotating. All agree, however, that centrifugal force is responsible for the bulge.

This exact line of thought convinced Newton that motion was *not* relative. He cited as proof the fact that if a bucket of water is rotated around a vertical axis, centrifugal force will cause the surface of the water to become concave or even to spill over the sides. It is unimaginable that a rotating universe could have this effect on the water; therefore, it must be concluded, Newton argued, that the bucket's rotation is absolute.

For ten years after he had published his special theory, Einstein brooded about this problem. Most physicists did not even see it as a problem. Why not face the fact, they said, that uniform motion is relative (as the special theory asserts), but that accelerated motion is absolute? Einstein was not satisfied with this state of affairs. He had a hunch that if uniform motion is relative, accelerated motion is also. Finally, in 1916, eleven years after the publication of his special theory, he published his General Theory of Relativity. The theory is called "general" because it is a generalization or extension of the special theory. It includes the special theory as a special case.

The general theory is a much greater intellectual achievement than the special theory. If Einstein had not been the first to conceive of the special theory, there is little doubt that other physicists would soon have thought of it. Poincaré, the French mathematician mentioned earlier, was one of several who came within a hair's breadth of it. In a remarkable speech that he gave in 1904,* Poincaré predicted that there would arise "an entirely new mechanics" in which no velocity can exceed that of light, just as no temperature can fall below absolute zero. It would maintain, he said, "the principle of relativity, according to which the laws of physical phenomena should be the same, whether for an observer fixed, or for an observer carried along in a uniform movement of translation; so that we have not any means of discerning whether or not we are carried along in such a motion." Poincaré did not see the essential steps that had to be taken in order to carry out such a program, but he certainly had an intuitive grasp on the essence of the special theory. At the time, Einstein was not aware of how closely the thoughts of Poincaré, Lorentz, and others were to his own. Years later he paid generous tribute to these men.

The General Theory of Relativity is an altogether different matter. It was, to use Teller's phrase again, "beautifully unexpected": a work of such stupendous originality, along such unorthodox lines, that it came into the scientific world with something like the same effect that the new dance craze, the twist, invaded in 1962 the ballrooms of the United States. Einstein had given a new twist to the ancient dance rhythms of time and space. In a surprisingly short time every physicist in the world was either dancing the new twist, expressing shocked horror over it, or complaining that he was too old to learn. If Einstein had not lived, no doubt other scientists would have given physics the same twist, but a century or more might have slipped by before they did so. Few other great theories in the history of science seem so completely the work of a single man.

"Newton, forgive me," Einstein wrote toward the end of his

---

* This speech is reprinted in the *Scientific Monthly* (April, 1956).

life. "You found the only way which, in your age, was just about possible for a man of highest thought and creative power." It is a moving tribute by the greatest scientist of our time to his greatest predecessor.

At the heart of Einstein's general theory is what he calls the Principle of Equivalence. This is nothing less than the staggering assertion (Newton would have considered it mad) that gravity and inertia are one and the same. This does not mean merely that they have similar effects. *Gravity and inertia are two different words for exactly the same thing.*

Einstein was not the first scientist to be impressed by the strange resemblance between gravitational and inertial effects. Consider for a moment just what happens when a cannonball and a small wooden ball are dropped from the same height. Assume that the cannonball's weight is one hundred times that of the wooden ball. This means that gravity pulls on the cannonball with a force that is one hundred times the force with which it pulls on the wooden ball. It is easy to understand why Galileo's enemies could not believe that two such balls would hit the ground at the same time. Of course we all now know that, ignoring the influence of air resistance, the balls fall side by side. To explain this fact, Newton had to assume something very curious. At the same time that gravity is pulling down on the cannonball, the ball's inertia—that is, its *resistance* to force—is holding back the cannon-

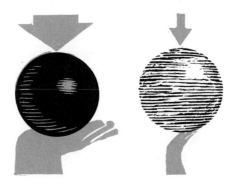

ball. True, the force of gravity is one hundred times greater on the cannonball than on the wooden ball, but the inertia holding back the cannonball is also exactly one hundred times greater!

Physicists often express it this way. The force of gravity on an object is always proportional to the object's inertia. If object A is twice as heavy as object B, its inertia is also twice as great. Twice as much force will be needed to accelerate object A to a certain speed as will be necessary to accelerate object B to the same speed. If this were not the case, objects of different weight would fall with different accelerations.

It is easy to imagine a world in which the two forces are not proportional. In fact, scientists imagined just such a world from the time of Aristotle to the time of Galileo! We could get along quite well in such a world. Conditions would not be exactly the same in a falling elevator, but how often does one ride in a falling elevator? As it is, we happen to live in a world in which the two forces are proportional. Galileo was the first to demonstrate this. Surprisingly accurate experiments confirming Galileo's findings were made around 1900 by a Hungarian physicist named Baron Roland von Eötvös. The most accurate tests of all were made in the past few years by a group of scientists at Princeton University. As far as they could determine, gravitational mass (weight) is always exactly proportional to inertial mass.

Newton knew, of course, about this curious tug-of-war between gravity and inertia, a tug-of-war that causes all objects to fall with the same acceleration, but he had absolutely no way of accounting for it. It was simply an extraordinary coincidence. Because of this coincidence it is possible to make use of inertia in such a way that gravitational fields can be both created and eliminated. The first chapter brought out that an artificial gravity field can be produced in a spaceship shaped like a torus (doughnut) simply by rotating the ship like a wheel. Centrifugal force will cause objects inside the ship to press against the outside rim. By rotating the ship at a certain constant speed, an inertial force field is created inside the ship that has the same effect as the gravitational field of the earth. Spacemen would walk about on

what they would regard as a curved floor. Dropped objects would fall to this floor. Smoke would rise to the ceiling. All the effects of a normal gravitational field would be present. Einstein illustrated the same point with the following famous thought experiment.

Imagine an elevator that is being pulled up through space with constantly increasing speed. If this acceleration is uniform, and exactly the same as the acceleration with which an object falls to the earth, then persons inside the elevator will believe themselves to be in a gravitational field exactly like the earth's.

Not only can acceleration counterfeit gravity in this way; it can also counteract gravity. In a falling elevator, for example, the downward acceleration completely eliminates the effect of gravity inside the car. A state of zero g (zero gravity) prevails inside a spaceship so long as it is in a state of free fall: moving freely under the influence of no force except gravity. The weightlessness experienced by Russian and American astronauts on their trips around the earth is explained by the fact that their ships are in a state of free fall as they circle the earth. So long as a spaceship's rocket motors are not working, there is zero g inside the ship.

This remarkable correspondence between inertia and gravity remained unexplained until Einstein developed his General Theory of Relativity. As in his special theory, he invoked the simplest, most daring hypothesis. In special relativity, remember, Einstein said that the reason there seems to be no ether wind is that there *isn't* any ether wind. In general relativity he says: The reason gravity and inertia seem to be the same thing is that they *are* the same thing.

It is not correct to say that inside an elevator, in a state of free fall, the earth's gravity is counteracted. Gravity is not counteracted, it is eliminated. The gravity actually disappears. Similarly, it is not correct to say that gravity in a rotating spaceship or an upward-accelerating elevator is counterfeited. In this case, gravity is not counterfeited, it is created. A gravitational field produced in this way does not have the same mathematical structure as a gravitational field surrounding a large body of matter like the earth, but it is nevertheless a genuine gravity field. As in the previous theory, the mathematical description of nature has to be complicated in order to make these startling statements hold true, but the end result justifies the complication. Instead of two separate forces, there is only one. Moreover, the theory leads to results that can be tested by observation and experiment.

Einstein's Principle of Equivalence—the equivalence of gravity and inertia—makes possible the view that all motion, including accelerated motion, is relative. This is how the trick is done. When Einstein's elevator is visualized as moving upward through the cosmos, with accelerating velocity, inertial effects can be observed inside the elevator. But the elevator can theoretically be made a fixed, motionless frame of reference. Now the entire universe, with all its galaxies, is moving down past the elevator with accelerating speed. *This accelerated motion of the universe generates a gravitational field.* The field causes objects inside the elevator to press against the floor. One can say that these effects are gravitational, not inertial.

But which is *really* happening? Is the elevator moving and causing inertial effects or is the universe moving and causing grav-

itational effects? This is not a proper question. There is no "real," absolute motion. There is only a relative motion of elevator and universe. This relative motion creates a force field, described by the field equations of the general theory. The field can be called either gravitational or inertial, depending on the choice of a frame of reference. If the elevator is the frame, the field is called gravitational. If the cosmos is the frame, the field is called inertial. Inertia and gravity are merely two different words that can be applied to the same situation. Naturally, it is much simpler, more convenient, to think of the universe as fixed. No one would consider calling the field gravitational. The General Theory of Relativity says, however, that the field *can* be called gravitational if a suitable frame of reference is adopted. No experiment that would prove this choice "wrong" can be performed inside such an elevator.

When it is said that the observer in the elevator cannot tell whether the field that is pressing him to the floor is inertial or gravitational, this does *not* mean that he cannot tell the difference between his field and a gravitational field surround-

ing a large body of matter, such as a planet. The gravitational field
around the earth, for example, has a spherical structure that cannot be duplicated by accelerating an elevator in space. If two
apples are held a foot apart and dropped from a great height
above the earth, they will move closer together as they fall, because each apple drops along a straight line aimed toward the
center of the earth. In the moving elevator, however, all objects
fall along parallel lines. This difference between the two fields
could be determined by tests inside the elevator, but the tests
would not distinguish between inertia and gravity. They would
distinguish only between fields with different mathematical struc-
tures.

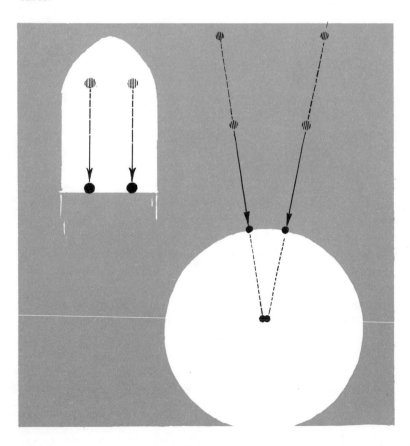

A similar situation is presented by the rotating earth. The ancient argument over whether the earth rotates or the heavens revolve around it (as Aristotle taught) is seen to be no more than an argument over the simplest choice of a frame of reference. Obviously, the most convenient choice is the universe. Relative to the universe, we say that the earth rotates and inertia makes its equator bulge. Nothing except inconvenience prevents us from choosing the earth as a fixed frame of reference. In the latter case, we say that the cosmos rotates around the earth, generating a gravitational field that acts upon the equator. Again, this field does not have the same mathematical structure as a gravitational field around a planet, but it can be called a true gravitational field nevertheless. If we choose to make the earth our fixed frame of reference, we do not even do violence to everyday speech. We say that the sun rises in the morning, sets in the evening; the Big Dipper revolves around the North Star. Which point of view is "correct"? Do the heavens revolve or does the earth rotate? The question is meaningless. A waitress might just as sensibly ask a customer if he wanted ice cream on top of his pie or the pie placed under his ice cream.

Think of the cosmos as having a kind of mysterious "grip" on every object in it. (Chapter 7 considers the question of where this grip comes from.) The odd thing about this grip is that once an object is moving uniformly through the universe, the universe offers no resistance to the motion. As soon as an attempt is made to force the object into nonuniform (accelerated) motion, the grip tightens. If the universe is made a fixed frame of reference, the grip is called the object's inertia: its resistance to the change of motion. If the object is made a fixed frame of reference, the grip is called gravitational: the universe's attempt to drag the object along as it (the universe) moves in a nonuniform way.

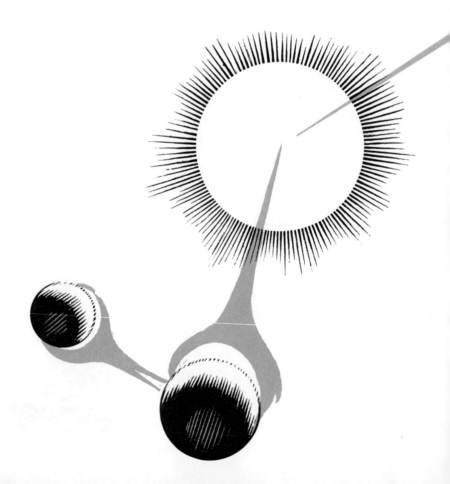

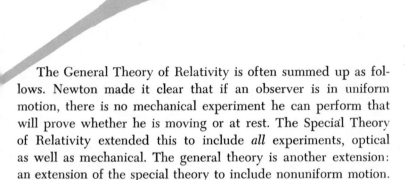

The General Theory of Relativity is often summed up as follows. Newton made it clear that if an observer is in uniform motion, there is no mechanical experiment he can perform that will prove whether he is moving or at rest. The Special Theory of Relativity extended this to include *all* experiments, optical as well as mechanical. The general theory is another extension: an extension of the special theory to include nonuniform motion. There is no experiment of any sort, the general theory says, by which an observer in *any* sort of motion, uniform or nonuniform, can prove whether he is moving or at rest.

The general theory is sometimes put this way. All the laws of nature are invariant (the same) with respect to any observer. This means that regardless of how an observer is moving, he can describe all the laws of nature (as he sees them) by the same mathematical equations. He may be a scientist working in a laboratory on the earth, or on the moon, or inside a giant spaceship that is slowly accelerating on its way to a distant star. The General Theory of Relativity provides him with a set of equations by which he can describe all the natural laws involved in any experiment he can perform. These equations will be exactly the same regardless of whether he is at rest, moving uniformly, or moving with acceleration with respect to any other object.

The next chapter takes a closer look at Einstein's theory of gravitation, and how it is related to an important new concept known as space-time.

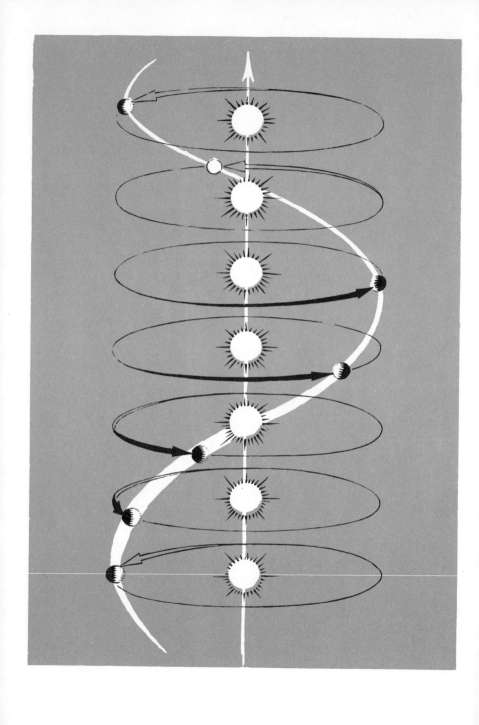

Gravity and
Space-Time

BEFORE anything can be said about Einstein's theory of gravity, it is necessary to make a few remarks, all too brief, about the fourth-dimension and non-Euclidian geometry. Hermann Minkowski, a Polish mathematician, gave relativity theory its elegant interpretation in terms of a four-dimensional space-time. Many of the ideas in this chapter are as much Minkowski's as they are Einstein's.

Consider a geometric point. It has no dimension. If it is moved in a straight line, it generates a line of one dimension. Move the line in a direction at right angles to itself and it generates a plane of two dimensions. Move the plane in a direction at right angles to itself and it generates a space of three dimensions. This is as far as we can go in our imagination. But a mathematician can

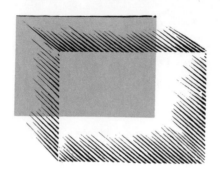

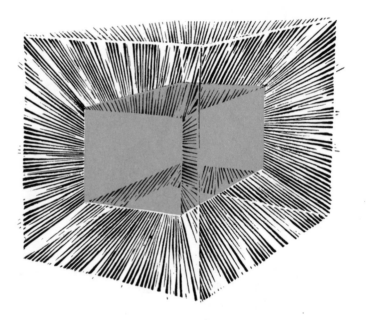

conceive (not in the sense of picturing it in his mind, but in the sense of working out the mathematics) of moving three-dimensional space in a direction at right angles to all three of its dimensions. This generates a Euclidian space of four dimensions. There is no need to stop at four. We can go on to spaces of five, six, seven, or more dimensions. All these spaces are Euclidian. They are extensions of Euclidian geometry in the same way that Euclidian solid geometry is an extension of Euclidian plane geometry.

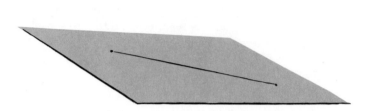

Euclidian geometry is based on a series of postulates of which one is the notorious parallel postulate. This postulate says that on a plane, through a given point outside a line, it is possible to draw one and only one line parallel to the given line. A Euclidian plane, to which this postulate applies, is said to be flat. It has zero curvature, infinite area. A non-Euclidian geometry is one in which the parallel postulate is replaced by another postulate. This can be done in two essentially different ways.

One way, called elliptic geometry, says that on the plane *no* line can be drawn through a point outside a line and parallel to that line. The surface of a sphere provides a rough, not exact, model of this type of non-Euclidian plane. The "straightest" possible line on the sphere is a great circle (a circle with a diameter equal to that of the sphere). All great circles intersect each other, so it is impossible for two great circles to be parallel. A non-

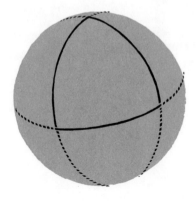

Euclidian plane of this type is said to have positive curvature. This curvature causes the plane to curve back on itself. It has a finite area instead of an infinite area.

The other type of non-Euclidian geometry, called hyperbolic geometry, is one in which the parallel postulate is replaced by a postulate which says that on a plane, through a point outside a line, there is an infinity of lines that are parallel to the given line. A rough model of a portion of this type of plane is provided by a saddle-shaped surface. Such a surface is said to have negative curvature. It does not close back on itself. Like the Euclidian plane, it extends to infinity in all directions.

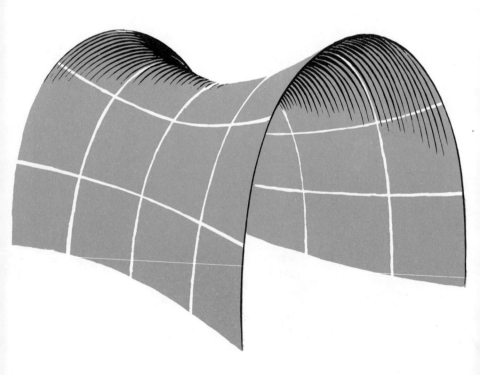

Both elliptic and hyperbolic geometry are non-Euclidian geometries of constant curvature. This means that the curvature is everywhere the same; objects do not undergo distortions as they move from one spot to another. A more general type of non-Euclidian geometry, usually called *general Riemannian geometry,* is one that permits the curvature to vary from point to point in any specified way.

Just as there are Euclidian geometries of 2, 3, 4, 5, 6, 7, . . . , dimensions, so also there are non-Euclidian geometries of 2, 3, 4, 5, 6, 7, . . . , dimensions.

In developing the General Theory of Relativity, Einstein found it necessary to adopt a four-dimensional general Riemannian geometry. Instead of a fourth space dimension, however, Einstein made *time* his fourth dimension. There is nothing mysterious or occult about this concept. It merely means that every event that takes place in the universe is an event occurring in a four-dimensional world of space-time.

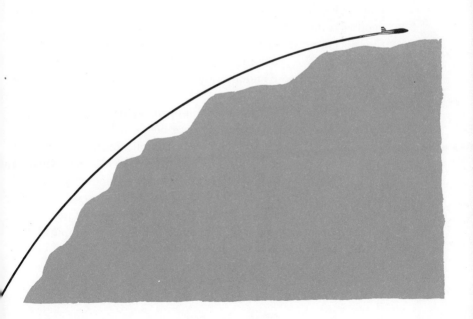

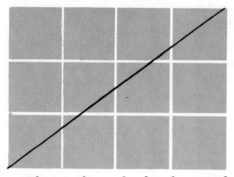

This can be made clear by considering the following event. You get into a car at 2 P.M. and drive from your home to a restaurant that is 3 miles south and 4 miles east of your house. On the two-dimensional plane the actual distance from your house to the restaurant is the hypotenuse of a right triangle with sides of 3 and 4 miles. This hypotenuse has a length of 5 miles. But it also took you a certain length of time, say 10 minutes, to make this drive. This time span can be shown on a three-dimensional graph. One coordinate of the graph is the distance south in miles, another is the distance east in miles, the vertical coordinate is the time in minutes. On this three-dimensional graph of space-time, the "interval" (space-time distance) between the two events (leaving your house and arriving at the restaurant) is shown as a straight line.

This straight line is not a graph of the actual trip. It is simply a measure of the space-time distance between the two events. A graph of the actual trip would be a complicated curved line. It would be complicated because your car accelerates when it starts, the arrangement of streets may make it impossible to drive to the restaurant on a straight line, perhaps you stopped at traffic lights along the way, and finally you had to accelerate negatively when you stopped the car. The complicated wavy graph of the actual trip is, in relativity theory, called the "world line" of the trip. In this case, it is a world line in a space-time of three dimensions, or (as it is sometimes called) in a Minkowski three-space.

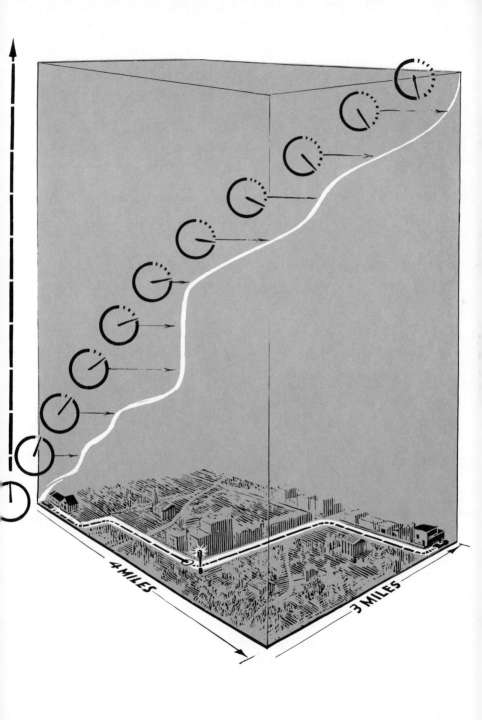

Because the trip by car took place on a plane of two dimensions, it was possible to add the one dimension of time and show the trip on a three-dimensional graph. When events occur in three-dimensional space it is not possible to draw an actual graph of four-dimensional space-time, but mathematicians have ways of handling such graphs without actually drawing them. Try to imagine a four-dimensional hyperscientist who can construct four-dimensional graphs as easily as the ordinary scientist can construct graphs with two and three dimensions. Three of the coordinates of his graph are the three dimensions of our space. The fourth coordinate is our time. If a spaceship leaves the earth and lands on Mars, our imaginary hyperscientist will draw the world line of this trip as a curve on his four-dimensional graph. (The line is curved because the ship cannot make such a trip without accelerating.) The space-time "interval" between take-off and landing will appear as a straight line on the graph.

In relativity theory, every object is a four-dimensional structure traveling along a world line in the four-dimensional world of space-time. If an object is considered at rest with respect to the three space coordinates, it is still traveling through the dimension of time. Its world line will be a straight line that is parallel with the time axis of the graph. If the object moves through space with uniform motion, its world line will still be straight, but no longer parallel with the time axis. If the object moves with nonuniform motion, its world line becomes curved.

We are now in position to look at the Lorentz-FitzGerald contractions of the special theory from a new point of view: the Minkowski point of view, or the viewpoint of our hyperscientist. As we have seen, when two spaceships pass each other in relative motion, observers on each ship see certain changes in the shape of the other ship as well as changes in the rate of the other ship's clock. This is because space and time are not absolutes that exist independently of each other. They are, so to speak, like shadow projections of a four-dimensional space-time object. If a book is held in front of a light and its shadow projected on a two-dimensional wall, a turn of the book will alter the shape of its shadow. With the book in one position the shadow is a fat rectangle.

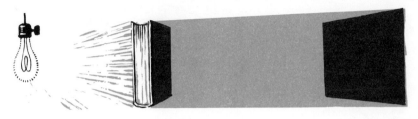

In another position it is a thin rectangle.

The book does not change its shape; only its two-dimensional shadow changes. In a smiliar way, an observer sees a four-dimensional structure, say a spaceship, in different three-dimensional projections depending on his motion relative to the structure. In some cases, the projection shows more of space and less of time; in other cases, the reverse is true. The changes that he observes in the space and time dimensions of the other ship can be explained by a kind of "rotation" of the ship in space-time, causing its shadow projections in space and time to alter. This is what Minkowksi had in mind when (in 1908) he began a famous lecture to the 80th Assembly of German Natural Scientists and Physicians. This lecture is reprinted in *The Principle of Relativity,* by Albert Einstein and others. No popular book on relativity is complete without this quotation:

> The views of space and time which I wish to lay before you have sprung from the soil of experimental physics, and therein lies their strength. They are radical. Henceforth space by itself, and time by itself, are doomed to fade away into mere shadows, and only a kind of union of the two will preserve an independent reality.

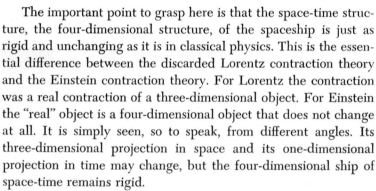

The important point to grasp here is that the space-time structure, the four-dimensional structure, of the spaceship is just as
rigid and unchanging as it is in classical physics. This is the essential difference between the discarded Lorentz contraction theory
and the Einstein contraction theory. For Lorentz the contraction
was a real contraction of a three-dimensional object. For Einstein
the "real" object is a four-dimensional object that does not change
at all. It is simply seen, so to speak, from different angles. Its
three-dimensional projection in space and its one-dimensional
projection in time may change, but the four-dimensional ship of
space-time remains rigid.

Here is another instance of how the theory of relativity introduces new absolutes. The four-dimensional shape of a rigid body
is an absolute, unchanging shape. Similarly, the four-dimensional
interval between any two events in space-time is an absolute
interval. Observers moving at great speeds and with different
relative motions may disagree on how far apart they judge two
events to be in space, and on how far apart they judge two events
to be in time, but *all* observers, regardless of their motions, will
agree on how far apart they judge two events to be in space-time.

In classical physics an object moves through space in a straight
line, with uniform velocity, unless acted upon by a force. A planet,
for example, would move off in a straight line were it not held by
the force of the sun's gravity. From this point of view, the sun is
said to "pull" the planet into an elliptical orbit.

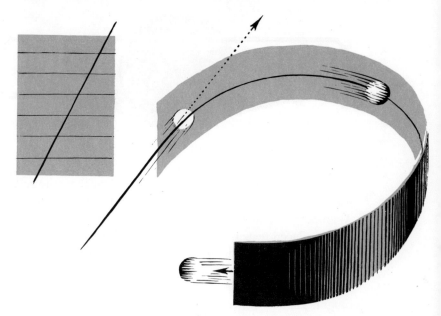

In relativity physics, an object also moves in a straight line, with uniform velocity, unless acted upon by a force, but the straight line must be thought of as a line in space-time instead of space. This is true even in the presence of gravity. The reason for this is that gravity, according to Einstein, is not a force at all! The sun does not "pull" on the planets. The earth does not "pull" down the falling apple. What happens is that a large body of matter, such as the sun, causes space-time to curve in the area surrounding it. The closer to the sun, the greater the curvature. In other words, the structure of space-time in the neighborhood of large bodies of matter becomes non-Euclidian. In this non-Euclidian space, objects continue to take the straightest possible paths, but what is straight in space-time is seen as curved when projected onto space. Our imaginary hyperscientist, if he plots the orbit of the earth on his four-dimensional graph, will plot it as a straight line. We who are three-dimensional creatures (more precisely, creatures who split up space-time into three-dimensional space and one-dimensional time) see the space path as an ellipse.

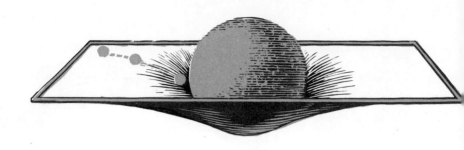

Writers on relativity theory often explain it in the following way. Imagine a rubber sheet stretched out flat like a trampoline. A grapefruit placed on this sheet will make a depression. A marble placed near the grapefruit will roll toward it. The grapefruit is not "pulling" the marble. Rather it has created a field (the depression) of such a structure that the marble, taking the path of least resistance, rolls toward the grapefruit. In a roughly (very roughly) similar way, space-time is curved or warped by the presence of large masses like the sun. This warping is the gravitational field. A planet moving around the sun is not moving in an ellipse because the sun pulls on it, but because the field is such that the ellipse is the straightest possible path the planet can take in space-time.

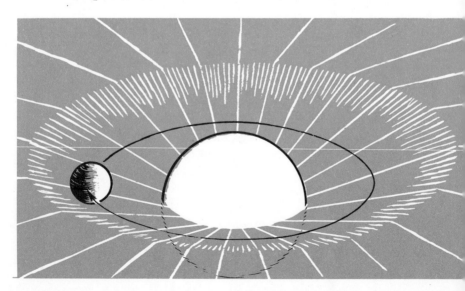

Such a path is called a geodesic. This is such an important word in relativity theory that it should be explained more fully. On a Euclidian plane, such as a flat sheet of paper, the straightest distance between two points is a straight line. It is also the shortest distance. On the surface of a globe, a geodesic between two points is the arc of a great circle. If a string is stretched as tautly as possible from point to point, it will mark out the geodesic. This too is both the straightest and the shortest distance connecting the two points.

In a four-dimensional *Euclidian* geometry, where all the dimensions are space dimensions, a geodesic also is the shortest and straightest line between two points. But in Einstein's *non-Euclidian* geometry of space-time, it is not so simple. There are three space dimensions and one time dimension, united in a way that is specified by the equations of relativity. This structure is such that a geodesic, although still the straightest possible path in space-time, is the *longest* instead of the shortest distance. This concept is impossible to explain without going into complicated

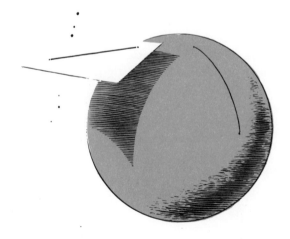

mathematics, but it has this curious result: A body, moving under the influence of gravity alone, always finds the path along which it takes the longest time to travel when the time is measured by its own clock. Bertrand Russell has called this the "law of cosmic laziness." The apple falls straight down, the missile moves in a parabola, the earth moves in an ellipse, because they are too lazy to take other routes.

It is this law of cosmic laziness that causes objects to move through space-time in ways sometimes attributed to inertia, sometimes to gravity. If you tie a string to an apple and swing it in circles, the string keeps the apple from moving in a straight line. We say that the apple's inertia pulls on the string. If the string breaks, the apple takes off in a straight line. Something like this happens when an apple falls off a tree. Before it falls, the branch prevents it from moving in a four-dimensional straight line. The apple on the branch is at rest (relative to the earth) but speeding through time because it is constantly getting older. If there were no gravitational field, this travel along the time coordinate would be graphed as a straight line on a four-dimensional graph. But the earth's gravity is curving space-time in the neighborhood of the apple. This forces the apple's world line to become a curve. When the apple breaks away from the branch, it continues to move through space-time, but (being a lazy apple) it now straightens its path and takes a geodesic. We see this geodesic as the apple's fall and attribute the fall to gravity. If we like, however, we can say that the apple's inertia, after the apple is suddenly released from its curved path, carries it to the ground.

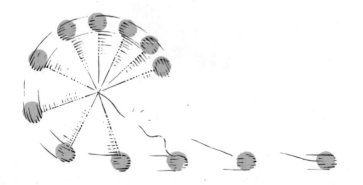

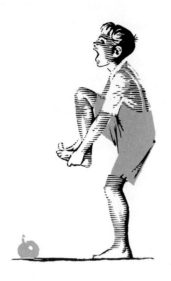

After the apple falls, suppose a boy comes along and kicks it with his bare foot. He shouts in pain because the kick hurts his toes. A Newtonian would say that the apple's inertia resisted his kick. An Einsteinian can say the same thing, but he can also say, if he prefers, that the boy's toes caused the entire cosmos (including the toes) to accelerate backward, setting up a gravitational field that pulled the apple with great force against his toes. It is all a matter of words. Mathematically, the situation is described by one set of space-time field equations; but it can be talked about informally (thanks to the Principle of Equivalence) in either of two sets of Newtonian phrases.

Although relativity theory replaces gravity by a geometrical warping of space-time, it leaves many basic questions still unanswered. Does this warping take place instantaneously through space or does it propagate like a wave motion? Most physicists think the warping moves like a wave and that it moves with the speed of light. There is even speculation that gravity waves consist of tiny indivisible particles of energy called "gravitons." So far, no experiment has yet detected either the waves or the gravitons.

Robert H. Dicke, a physicist at Princeton University, thinks gravity is slowly getting weaker and may now be 13 per cent less strong than it was four or five billion years ago when the earth was formed. If this is true, the earth is probably expanding and its surface cracking in the process. The sun, also, would be expanding. Two billion years ago it would have been smaller, denser, and hotter; a fact that would explain the tropical conditions that seem to have prevailed over most of the earth in earlier geological epochs. All these are just guesses at present, but it may soon be possible to devise experiments that will test Dicke's theory,

Relativity theory furnishes a new way of looking at gravity and describing it, but it still remains a mysterious, little-understood phenomenon. No one knows what connection it has, if any, with electromagnetism. Einstein and others have tried to develop a "unified field theory" that will unite gravity and electromagnetism in one set of mathematical equations. The results have been disappointing. Perhaps some young reader of these words, if he has the creative genius of an Einstein, will some day see how to formulate such a theory.

Has the General Theory of Relativity been confirmed by experimental evidence? Yes, though not nearly so thoroughly as the special theory. The first confirmation had to do with the orbit of Mercury, the planet nearest the sun. Mercury's orbit is an ellipse, but the ellipse itself rotates slowly. Newton's equations for gravity account for this, on the basis of the influence of the other planets, but predict a slightly slower rotation than what is actually observed. Einstein's equations predict a rotation of a planet's elliptical orbit even in the absence of other planets; in the case of Mercury the predicted orbit is much closer to the actual one than the orbit predicted by Newton. The other planets have orbits that are more circular, so the effect is harder to observe, but in recent years there have been measurements of the rotation of the orbits of both Venus and the earth that are in good agreement with Einstein's equations.

A second prediction made by Einstein was that light from the sun would show an extremely minute shift toward the red. According to the equations of the general theory, strong gravitational fields have a slowing effect on time. This means that any rhythmic process, such as the vibrations of atoms or the ticking of a clock, would take place on the sun at a slightly lower rate than on the earth. This in turn would shift the spectrum of sunlight toward the red. Such a shift has been observed, but it is subject to so many other interpretations that it does not provide very strong evidence.° A white dwarf star very close to Sirius, known as the companion of Sirius, is massive enough to produce a red shift thirty times that of the sun. This too has been observed, providing stronger confirmation. However, the strongest confirmations of gravity's effect on time have recently been obtained in the laboratory. They will be described at the close of Chapter 8.

The most dramatic of all tests of the general theory took place in 1919 during a total eclipse of the sun. Einstein had reasoned as follows: If an elevator in interstellar space were pulled upward with an accelerating velocity, a light beam traveling from side to side inside the elevator would bend down in a parabolic path. This would be regarded as an inertial effect, but according to the

° *Scientific American,* March 1962, reports on the most recent and accurate measurements yet made of the solar red shift. Using an entirely new method, J. E. Blamont and F. Roddier of the Meudon Observatory in France, found a red shift in the absorption line of strontium that is so close to the shift predicted by general relativity that it provides for the first time a high degree of confirmation. As the magazine put it, "the unprecedented accuracy" of the measurement "has apparently laid to rest a skeleton that has been rattling in the closet of physics for more than 40 years."

general theory, one can make the elevator a fixed frame of reference and view the curving of the beam as a gravitational effect. Gravity, then, is capable of curving light beams. The curving is much too minute to be detected by any laboratory experiment, but it can be measured by astronomers during a total eclipse of the sun. Because the sun's light is blocked off by the moon, stars very close to the sun's edge become visible. Light from these stars passes through the strongest part of the sun's gravitational field. Any shift in the apparent positions of these stars would indicate that the sun's gravity was bending their light. The greater the shift, the greater the bend.

A word of caution: When you read about the "bending" of light by gravity or inertia, you must remember that this is just a three-dimensional way of speaking. In space the light does indeed curve. But in Minkowski's four-dimensional world of space-time, light continues, as in classical physics, to move along geodesics. It takes the straightest possible path. Our imaginary four-dimensional scientist would always graph the path of a light beam as a straight line on his chart of space-time, even when it passed through strong gravitational fields.

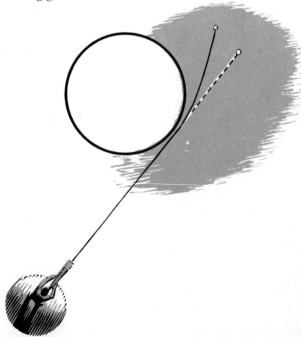

Arthur Stanley Eddington, the English astronomer, was in charge of an expedition of scientists that went to Africa in 1919 to observe the total eclipse of the sun. The primary purpose of the expedition was to make accurate measurements of the positions of stars close to the sun's rim. Newton's physics also suggested a bending of light in gravitational fields, but Einstein's equations predicted a deflection about twice as large. So there were at least three possible outcomes of the test:

1. There would be no change in the positions of the stars.

2. The deflection would be close to what Newtonian physics had predicted.

3. The deflection would be close to what Einstein had predicted.

The first outcome would damage both Newton's equations and those of the General Theory of Relativity. The second would strengthen Newton, discredit Einstein. The third would discredit Newton, strengthen Einstein. According to a story that made the rounds at the time, two astronomers on the expedition were discussing the three possibilities.

"And what," said one of them, "if we get a deflection twice as big as Einstein predicted?"

"Then," said the other, "Eddington will go mad."

Happily, the deflection proved to be close to Einstein's prediction. It was the publicity surrounding this dramatic confirmation of general relativity that first brought the theory to the attention of the general public. Today, astronomers are inclined to be sceptical of this confirmation. The difficulties in making precise measurements of star positions during an eclipse are much greater than Eddington supposed, and there have been differences in the results obtained during various eclipses since 1919. At a meeting of the Royal Society of London, in February 1962, a group of scientists discussed this question. They concluded that the difficulties are so great that eclipse observers should no longer attempt such measurements.

Just as there are experiments (all too few) that have confirmed general relativity, and countless experiments as yet untried and even unthought of that might confirm it even more, so there are possible experiments which might strongly discredit the theory. George Gamow, a well-known physicist at the University of Colorado, has described one such experiment involving antiparticles.° Antiparticles are known to have positive inertial mass; it has been conjectured that they may have negative gravitational mass. If so, any gravitational force acting upon them would cause them to accelerate in a negative direction. An antiapple made of antimatter would have flown up in the sky instead of falling on Newton's nose. Whether antiparticles have negative gravitational mass has not yet been determined, but if they do, relativity theory will be in serious trouble.

To understand why there would be a difficulty, imagine a spaceship suspended in interstellar space, motionless with respect to the stars. Floating inside the spaceship is a solitary antiapple with negative gravitational mass. The ship starts to move in the direction of the ceiling with an acceleration of one g. (A "g" is the acceleration with which bodies fall to the earth: about 32 feet per second per second. This means that every second the speed increases by 32 feet per second.)

What happens to the apple?

° See Gamow's article on gravity in *The Scientific American* (March, 1961).

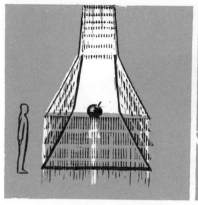

From the standpoint of an observer outside the ship, attached to the inertial frame of the cosmos, the apple should stay right where it is relative to the stars. No force is acting on it. The ship itself does not touch the apple; the ship might just as well be a thousand miles away. The floor of the compartment should, therefore, move up until it hits the apple. (We don't have to worry, in this thought experiment, about what happens when the floor hits the apple.)

The situation is altogether different if the ship is taken as a fixed frame of reference. Now the observer must suppose a gravitational field acting inside the ship. This would send the apple toward the ceiling with an acceleration (relative to the stars) of two *g*. A basic principle of relativity has been violated: The two frames of reference are not interchangeable.

In other words, negative gravitational mass is difficult to reconcile with general relativity, although Newton's approach to inertia accommodates it easily. Classical physics simply takes the first point of view. The ship has an absolute motion with respect to the ether. The apple remains at absolute rest. No gravitational field enters to complicate the picture.

The discovery of negative gravitational mass and the effect of antigravity would, concludes Gamow, "force upon us a choice between Newton's law of inertia and Einstein's equivalence principle. The author earnestly hopes that this will not come to pass."

Mach's
Principle

EINSTEIN's Principle of Equivalence says that when an object is accelerated or rotated, a force field is created which can be looked upon either as inertial or gravitational, depending on the choice of a reference frame. A question of great importance now arises; a question that leads quickly into deep, yet-unsolved problems.

Are these force fields the result of motion with respect to a space-time structure that exists independently of matter, or is the space-time structure *created* by matter; that is to say, created by the galaxies and other material bodies of the universe?

Experts divide. All the old eighteenth-century and nineteenth-century arguments over whether "space" or the "ether" has an existence apart from matter are still with us; only now they are arguments about the space-time structure (sometimes called the "metrical field") of the cosmos. Most of the early writers on relativity—Arthur Stanley Eddington, Bertrand Russell, Alfred North Whitehead, and others—believed that the structure is independent of the stars, though of course it is given local distortions by the stars. More plainly, if there were no other objects in the cosmos except the earth, it would still be possible, so these writers contended, for the earth to rotate relative to this space-time structure. (It is irrelevant to this argument whether the structure has an over-all positive, negative, or zero curvature.) A lone spaceship, the sole object in the universe, could still turn on its rocket motors and accelerate. Inside the ship, astronauts would still feel the inertial forces of acceleration. A lone earth, rotating in space, would still bulge around its middle. It would bulge because particles of its matter would be forced into paths that were not geodesics in the space-time structure. The particles would go, so to speak, against the natural "grain" of space-time. It would even be possible, on such a lone earth, to measure a type of inertial force called the Coriolis force * and determine the *direction* in which the earth was spinning.

* If an intercontinental missile is traveling north or south, the rotation of the earth tends to deflect it to the right in the northern hemisphere, to the left in the southern hemisphere. This inertial effect is called the Coriolis force after G. G. Coriolis, an early nineteenth-century French engineer who was the first to analyze it completely. Cyclones and other circular movements of the atmosphere are directly traceable to Coriolis forces. See "The Coriolis Effect" by James E. McDonald, in *Scientific American* (May, 1952). (Reprinted in *New Worlds of Modern Science*, ed. Leonard Engel. New York: Dell Books, 1956.)

Einstein granted the possible truth of this view, but he did not (at least as a young man) find it to his taste. He preferred instead a point of view that had first been advanced by the Irish philosopher, Bishop Berkeley. If the earth were the only body in the universe, Berkeley argued, it would be meaningless to say that it could rotate. Somewhat similar views were held in the seventeenth century by the German philosopher Gottfried von Leibniz and the Dutch physicist Christian Huygens, but it remained for Ernst Mach (the Austrian physicist mentioned on page 21) to back up this view with a plausible scientific theory. Mach anticipated much of relativity theory, and Einstein has written about the extent to which Mach inspired his early thinking. (Sad to relate, Mach in his old age, after his insights had been incorporated by Einstein into a successful theory, refused to accept relativity.)

From Mach's point of view, a cosmos without stars would have no space-time structure relative to which the earth could spin. For there to be gravitational (or inertial) fields capable of bulging a planet's equator and spilling water over the sides of a rotating bucket, there must be stars to create a space-time structure. Without such a structure, space-time would possess no geodesics. It could not even be said that a light beam, speeding through completely empty space, would travel in a geodesic, because in the absence of a space-time structure the beam would not know how to take one path rather than another. As expressed by one writer, A. d'Abro (in his excellent book, *The Evolution of Scientific Thought*), it would not know which way to go. Even the existence of a spherical body such as the earth might be impossible. Particles of earth are packed together by gravity, and gravity moves particles along geodesics. With no space-time structure and no geodesics, the earth (as d'Abro says) would not know what shape to take. Eddington once expressed this point humorously: In an entirely empty universe (if Mach is correct), Einstein's gravitational fields would fall to the ground!

D'Abro describes a thought experiment that helps clarify Mach's position. Imagine an astronaut floating in space. He is the only object in the universe. In his hand he holds a brick. We know that the brick would have no weight (gravitational mass). Would it have inertial mass? If the astronaut tried to heave the brick into space, would it resist the movement of his hand? From Mach's point of view it would not. With no stars in the cosmos to provide a metrical field for space-time, there is nothing relative to which the brick can accelerate. Of course, there is the astronaut, but his mass is so small that any effect relative to him would be negligible.

Einstein used the term "Mach's principle" for Mach's point of view. It was Einstein's early hope that this view could be incorporated into relativity theory. In fact, he once devised a model of the universe (to be discussed in Chapter 9) in which the space-time structure of the universe has no existence except insofar as it is created by the stars and other material bodies. "In a consistent theory of relativity," Einstein wrote in 1917 when he published his first mathematical description of this model, "there can be no inertia relative to 'space,' but only an inertia of masses relative to one another. If, therefore, I have a mass at a sufficient distance from all other masses in the universe, its inertia must fall to zero."

Later, serious flaws were discovered in Einstein's cosmic model and he was forced to abandon Mach's principle, but the principle continues to exert a strong fascination over today's cosmologists. It is not difficult to see why. It carries the relativity of motion to its ultimate. The opposing point of view, the view that assumes a space-time metric even in the absence of stars, is really very close to the old ether theory. Instead of a motionless, invisible jelly called the ether, there is a motionless, invisible space-time structure. By assuming this to be fixed, accelerations and rotations take on a suspiciously absolute character. In fact, proponents of this point of view have not hesitated to speak of rotations and accelerations as "absolute." But if inertial effects are relative, not to such a structure but only to a structure generated by the stars, then a very pure form of relativity is preserved.

Dennis Sciama, an English cosmologist, has developed an ingenious theory along Machian lines. He gives an entertaining account of it in his popularly written book, *The Unity of the Universe*. According to Sciama, inertial effects due to rotation or acceleration are the result of a relative motion with respect to the total matter in the universe. If this is true, then a measurement of inertia provides a method for estimating the amount of matter in the universe! Sciama's equations show that the influence of nearby stars on inertia is astonishingly small. All the stars in our galaxy, he believes, contribute only about one ten-millionth of the strength of inertia on the earth. Most of its strength is contributed by distant galaxies. Sciama estimates that 80 percent of inertial force is the result of motion relative to galaxies so distant that they have not yet been discovered by our telescopes!

In Mach's day it was not known that galaxies other than our own existed, nor was it known that our galaxy rotates. Astronomers today know that centrifugal force, arising from rotation, causes our galaxy to bulge enormously. From Mach's point of view this bulge could occur only if vast quantities of matter existed outside the galaxy. Had Mach known of the inertial effect of rotation on our galaxy, Sciama points out, he would have been able to deduce the existence of other galaxies fifty years before any of them were discovered.

Perhaps the startling character of Sciama's point of view can be made even more evident by the following illustration. I once owned a small glass-topped puzzle, shaped like a square and containing four steel balls. Each ball rested on a groove that ran from the square's center to one of its corners. The problem was to get all four balls into the corners at the same time. The only way to solve it was by placing the puzzle flat on a table and spinning it. Centrifugal force did the trick. If Sciama is right, this puzzle could not be solved in this way if it were not for the existence of billions of galaxies at enormous distances from our own.

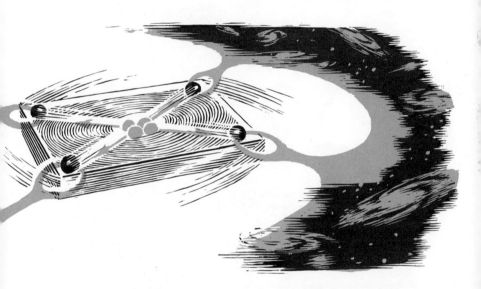

Will the future of relativity theory move in the direction of Mach and Sciama, or will it retain an absolute structure of space-time, independent of the stars? No one can say. If a successful field theory is developed, in which the elementary particles of matter can be explained in terms of a space-time field, then the stars themselves will become merely one aspect of that field. Instead of stars generating the structure, the structure will generate the stars. At the moment, however, all this is idle speculation.

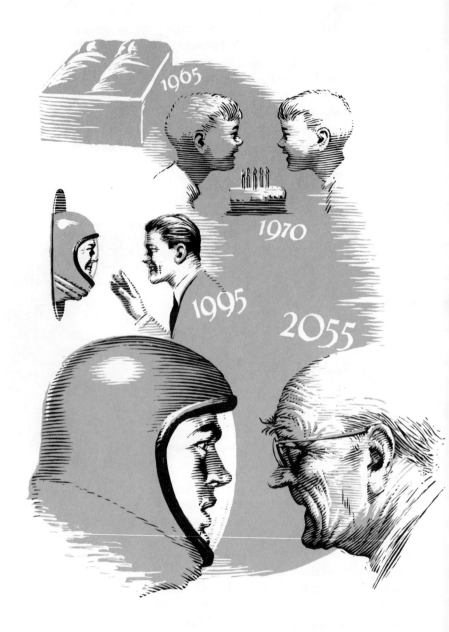

The Twin
Paradox

How did the world's leading scientists and philosophers react when they caught their first glimpse of the strange new world of relativity? The reaction was mixed. Most physicists and astronomers, confused by the violations of common sense and the difficult mathematics of the general theory, maintained a discreet silence. But scientists and philosophers capable of understanding relativity were inclined to accept it with exhilaration. It has already been mentioned how quickly Eddington perceived the greatness of Einstein's achievement. Moritz Schlick, Bertrand Russell, Rudolf Carnap, Ernst Cassirer, Alfred North Whitehead, Hans Reichenbach, and many other eminent philosophers were early enthusiasts who wrote about the theory and tried to clarify its implications. Russell's book, *The ABC of Relativity*, was first published in 1925 but is still one of the best popular accounts of relativity ever written.

Here and there scientists were unable to shake themselves loose from old Newtonian habits of thought. In many ways they resembled the scientists back in the days of Galileo who could not bring themselves to admit that Aristotle might have been mistaken. Michelson himself, a limited mathematician, never accepted relativity, even though his great experiment paved the way for the special theory. As late as 1935, when I was an undergraduate at the University of Chicago, I took a course in astronomy from Professor William D. Macmillan, a widely respected scientist. He was openly scornful of relativity.

"We of the present generation are too impatient to wait for anything," Macmillan wrote in 1927. "Within forty years of Michelson's failure to detect the expected motion of the earth with respect to the ether we have wiped out the slate, made a postulate that by no means whatever can the thing be done, and constructed a non-Newtonian mechanics to fit the postulate. The success which has been attained is a marvelous tribute to our intellectual activity and our ingenuity, but I am not so sure with respect to our judgment." *

All sorts of objections were raised against relativity. One of the earliest, most persistent objections centered around a paradox that had first been mentioned in 1905 by Einstein himself, in his paper on special relativity. (The word "paradox" is used in the sense of something opposed to common sense, not something logically contradictory.) This paradox is very much in the scientific news today because advances in space flight, coupled with progress in building fantastically accurate timing devices, may soon provide a way to test the paradox in a very direct manner.

The paradox is usually described as a thought experiment involving twins. They synchronize their watches. One twin gets

---

* From Macmillan's contribution to *A Debate on the Theory of Relativity*, by Robert D. Carmichael and others, La Salle, Ill.: Open Court Publishing Company, 1927.

into a spaceship and makes a long trip through space. When he returns, the twins compare watches. According to the Special Theory of Relativity, the traveler's watch will show a slightly earlier time. In other words, time on the spaceship will have gone at a slower rate than time on the earth. So long as the space journey is confined to the solar system, and made at relatively low speeds, this time difference will be negligible. But over long distances, with velocities close to that of light, the "time dilation" (as it is sometimes called) can be large. It is not inconceivable that someday a means will be found by which a spaceship can be slowly accelerated until it reaches a speed only a trifle below that of light. This would make possible visits to other stars in the galaxy, perhaps even trips to other galaxies. So, the twin paradox is more than just a parlor puzzle; someday it may become a common experience of space travelers.

Suppose that the astronaut twin goes a distance of 1,000 light-years and returns: a small distance compared with the diameter of our galaxy. Would not the astronaut surely die long before he completes the trip? Would not his trip require, as in so many science-fiction stories, an entire colony of men and women so that generations would live and die while the ship was making its long interstellar voyage?

The answer depends on how fast the ship goes. If it travels just under the limiting speed of light, time within the ship will proceed at a much slower rate. Judged by earth-time the trip will, of course, take more than 2,000 years. Judged by the astronaut on the ship, if he travels fast enough, the trip may take only a few decades!

For readers who like specific figures, here is a recent calculation by Edwin M. McMillan, a nuclear physicist at the University of California, in Berkeley. An astronaut travels from the earth to the spiral nebula in Andromeda. It is about 2 million light-years away. He makes the trip by going half the distance with a constant acceleration of 2 g, then he accelerates negatively at 2 g until he reaches the nebula. (This is a convenient way, incidentally, of maintaining a steady gravity field inside a space-

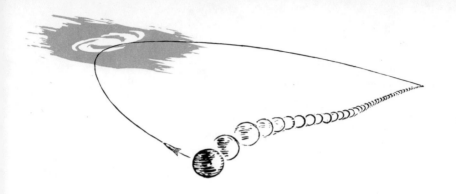

ship for the entire duration of a long trip, without rotating the ship.) The procedure is repeated for the return trip. According to the astronaut's own clock, the trip takes 29 years. According to earth clocks, almost 3 million years have gone by!

You can see at once that this raises all sorts of fascinating possibilities. A scientist of 40 and his teen-age laboratory assistant fall in love. They feel that their age difference makes a marriage out of the question. So off he goes on a long space voyage, traveling close to the speed of light. He returns, age 41. Meanwhile, on the earth his girlfriend has become a woman of 33. Perhaps she could not wait 15 years for her lover to return; she has married someone else. The scientist cannot bear this. Off he goes on another long trip. Moreover, he is curious to know if a certain theory he has published is going to be confirmed or discarded by later generations. He returns to earth, age 42. His former girlfriend is long since dead. What is worse, his pet theory has been demolished. Humiliated, he takes an even longer trip, returning at the age of 45 to see what the world is like a few thousand years hence. Perhaps, like the time traveler in H. G. Wells' story "The Time Machine," he will find that humanity has become obsolete. Now he is stranded. Wells' time machine could go both ways, but our lonely scientist has no means of getting back into the stream of human history where he belongs.

Unusual moral questions would arise if this sort of time travel became possible. Is there anything wrong, for instance, in a girl marrying her own great-great-great-great-great-great-grandson?

Please note: This kind of time travel avoids all the logical traps that plague science fiction, such as dropping into the past to kill your parents before you are born, or whisking into the future and shooting yourself between the eyes. Consider, for example, the plight of Miss Bright in that familiar limerick:

> There was a young lady named Bright,
> Who traveled much faster than light.
> She started one day
> In the relative way,
> And returned on the previous night.

If she returned on the previous night, then she must have encountered a duplicate of herself. Otherwise it would not have been truly the night before. But there could not have been two Miss Brights the night before because the time-traveling Miss Bright left with no memory of having met her duplicate yesterday. So you see, there is a clear-cut contradiction. Time travel of *that* sort is not logically possible unless the existence of parallel

worlds running along different time tracks is assumed. Even with this gimmick, matters become quite complicated.

Note also that Einstein's form of time travel does not confer upon the traveler any genuine immortality, or even longevity. As far as *he* is concerned he always ages at the normal rate. It is only the earth's "proper time" that for the traveler seems to gallop along at breakneck speed.

Henri Bergson, the famous French philosopher, was the most eminent thinker to cross swords with Einstein over the twin paradox. He wrote about it at some length, poking fun at what he thought were its logical absurdities. Unfortunately, what he wrote only proves that it is possible to be a great philosopher without knowing much about mathematics. In the last few years the same objections have been raised again. Herbert Dingle, an English physicist, is most vocal today in refusing to believe the paradox. For years he has been writing witty articles about it and accusing other relativity experts of being either obtuse or evasive. The superficial analysis to be given here certainly will not clear up this controversy, which quickly plunges into complicated equations, but it will explain in a general way why there is almost universal agreement among experts that the twin paradox will really carry through in just the manner Einstein described.

Dingle's objection, the strongest that can be made against the paradox, is stated this way. According to the General Theory of Relativity, there is no absolute motion of any sort, no "preferred" frame of reference. It is always possible to choose a moving object as a fixed frame of reference without doing violence to any natural law. When the earth is chosen as a frame, the astronaut makes the long journey, returns, finds himself younger than his stay-at-home brother. All well and good. But what happens when the spaceship is taken as the frame of reference? Now it must be assumed that the earth makes a long journey away from the ship and back again. In this case it is the twin on the ship who is the stay-at-home. When the earth gets back to the spaceship, will not the earth rider be the younger? If so, the situation is more than a paradoxical affront to common sense; it

is a flat logical contradiction. Clearly each twin cannot be younger
than the other.

Dingle likes to state it this way: Either the assumption must
be made that after the trip the twins will be exactly the same
age, or relativity must be discarded.

Without going into any of the actual computations, it is not
hard to understand why the alternatives are not so drastic as
Dingle would have us believe. It is true that all motion is relative, but in this case, there is one all-important difference between the relative motion of the astronaut and the relative motion of the stay-at-home. *The stay-at-home does not move relative
to the universe.*

How does this affect the paradox?

Assume that the astronaut is off to visit Planet X, somewhere
in the galaxy. He travels at a constant speed. The stay-at-home's
watch is attached to the inertial frame of the earth, on which
there is agreement among clocks because they are all relatively
motionless with respect to each other. The astronaut's watch is
attached to a different inertial frame, the frame of the ship. If the
ship just kept on going forever there would be no paradox because there would be no way to compare the two watches. But
the ship has to stop and turn around at Planet X. When it does
so, there is a change from an inertial frame moving away from
the earth to a new inertial frame moving toward the earth. This
shift is accompanied by enormous inertial forces as the ship accelerates during the turn-around. In fact, if the acceleration during the turn-around were too great, the astronaut (and not his
twin on the earth) would be killed. These inertial forces arise,
of course, because the astronaut is accelerating with respect to
the universe. They do not arise on the earth because the earth is
not undergoing similar acceleration.

From one point of view it can be said that the inertial forces
produced by this acceleration "cause" a slowing-down of the
astronaut's watch; from another point of view the acceleration
merely indicates a shift of inertial frames. Because of this shift,
the world line of the spaceship, its path when plotted on Minkow-

ski's four-dimensional graph of space-time, becomes a path on which the total "proper time" of the round trip is less than the total proper time along the world line of the stay-at-home twin. *
Although acceleration is involved in the shifting of inertial frames, the actual computation involves nothing more than the equations of the special theory.

Dingle's objection still remains, however, because exactly the same calculations can be made by supposing that the spaceship instead of the earth is the fixed frame of reference. Now it is the earth that moves away, shifts inertial frames, comes back again. Why wouldn't the same calculations, with the same equations, show that earth-time slowed down the same way? They would indeed if it were not for one gigantic fact: When the earth moves away, *the entire universe moves with it*. When the earth executes its turn-around, the universe does also. This accelerating universe generates a powerful gravitational field. As was explained on page 101, gravity has a slowing effect on clocks. A clock on the sun, for instance, would tick more slowly than the same clock on earth, more slowly on the earth than on the moon. Now it turns out, when all the proper calculations are made, that the gravitational field generated by the accelerating cosmos slows down the spaceship clocks until they differ from earth clocks by precisely the same amount as before. This gravity field has, of course, no effect on earth clocks. The earth does not move relative to the cosmos; therefore, there is no gravitational field with respect to the earth.

It is instructive to imagine a situation in which the same time difference results, even though no accelerations are involved. Spaceship A passes the earth with uniform speed, on its way to Planet X. As the ship passes the earth it sets its clock at zero time. Ship A continues with uniform velocity to Planet X where it passes spaceship B, moving with uniform speed in the opposite direction. As the ships pass, A radios to B the amount of time

---

* To see exactly how this works out mathematically read the excellent article on "The Clock Paradox in Relativity Theory," by Alfred Schild in *American Mathematical Monthly* (January, 1959).

(measured by its own clock) that has elapsed since it passed the earth. Ship B notes this information, and continues with uniform speed to the earth. As it passes the earth it radios to the earth the length of time A took to make the trip from the earth to Planet X, together with the length of time it took B (measured by its own clock) to make the trip from Planet X to earth. The total of these two periods of time will be less than the time (measured by earth clocks) that has elapsed between the moment that ship A passed the earth and the moment that ship B passed the earth.

This difference in time can be calculated by the equations of the special theory. No accelerations of any sort are involved. Of course, now there is no twin paradox because there is no astronaut who goes out and comes back. It can be supposed that the traveling twin rides out on ship A, then transfers to ship B and rides back, but there is no way he can do this without transferring from one inertial frame to another. To make the transfer he must undergo incredibly strong inertial forces. These forces indicate his shift of inertial frames. If we wish, we can say that the inertial forces slow down his clock. However, if the whole episode is viewed from the standpoint of the traveling twin, taking him as the fixed frame of reference, then a shifting cosmos that sets up gravitational fields enters the picture. (A major source of confusion in discussing the twin paradox is that the situation can be described in so many different verbal ways.) Regardless of the point of view adopted, the equations of relativity give the same time difference. This difference can be accounted for by the special theory alone. It is only to counter the objection raised by Dingle that the general theory must be brought into the picture.

It cannot be stated too often that it is not correct to ask which situation is "right": Does the traveling twin move out and back or does the stay-at-home and cosmos move out and back? There is only *one* situation: a relative motion of the twins. There are, however, two different ways of talking about it. In one language, a change of inertial frames on the part of the astronaut, with its resulting inertial forces, accounts for the difference in aging. In the other language, gravitational forces overbalance the effect of a change of inertial frames on the part of the earth. *From either point of view the stay-at-home and the cosmos do not move relative to one another.* Thus the situation is entirely different for each man, even though the relativity of motion is strictly preserved. The paradoxical difference in aging is accounted for, regardless of which twin is taken to be at rest. There is no need to discard the theory of relativity.

An interesting question can now be asked: What if the cosmos contained nothing except two spaceships, A and B? Ship A turns on its rocket engines, makes a long trip, comes back. Would the previously synchronized clocks on the two ships be the same?

The answer depends on whether you adopt Eddington's view of inertia or the Machian view of Dennis Sciama. In Eddington's view the answer is "yes." Ship A accelerates with respect to the metric space-time structure of the cosmos; ship B does not. The situation remains unsymmetrical and the usual difference in aging results. From Sciama's point of view the answer is "no." Acceleration is meaningless except with respect to other material bodies. In this case, the only material bodies are the two spaceships. The situation is perfectly symmetrical. In fact, there are no inertial frames to speak of, because there is no inertia (except an extremely feeble, negligible inertia resulting from the presence of the two ships). In a cosmos without inertia it is hard to predict what would happen if a ship turned on its rocket motors! As Sciama says, with English understatement, "Life would be quite different in such a universe."

Because the slowing of the traveling twin's time can be viewed as a gravitational effect, any experiment that shows a slowing of time by gravity provides a kind of indirect confirmation of the twin paradox. In recent years there have been several such confirmations by means of a wonderful new laboratory tool called the Mössbauer effect. A young German physicist named Rudolf L. Mössbauer discovered, in 1958, how to make a "nuclear clock" that keeps unbelievably accurate time. Imagine one clock ticking five times every second and another clock ticking at so nearly the same rate that after a million million ticks it has lost only one hundredth of a tick. The Mössbauer effect is capable of detecting at once that the second clock is slower than the first! Experiments using the Mössbauer effect have shown that time near the bottom of a building (where gravity is stronger) is a bit slower than time near the top of the same building. "A typist working on the first floor of the Empire State Building," Gamow has observed, "will age slower than her twin sister working on the top floor." The difference in aging is, of course, infinitesimal; nevertheless, it is real and can be measured.

English physicists have also discovered, using the Mössbauer effect, that a nuclear clock slows down a bit when placed on the edge of a rapidly rotating disk as small as six inches in diameter. The revolving clock can be viewed as the traveling twin who undergoes constant changes of inertial frames (or alternatively, as the twin affected by a gravitational field if the disk is assumed at rest and the cosmos rotating), so this provides the most direct test yet of the twin paradox. An even more direct test will be made when a nuclear clock is placed in an artificial satellite, sent whirling at great speed around the earth, then recovered and compared with a stay-at-home clock. Of course, the time is rapidly approaching when an astronaut can make the final, definitive test by carrying a nuclear clock with him on a long space voyage. No physicist except Professor Dingle doubts that the astronaut's clock, when he returns, will be slightly out of phase with a nuclear clock that stayed at home.

Still, one must always be prepared for surprises. Remember the Michelson-Morley experiment!

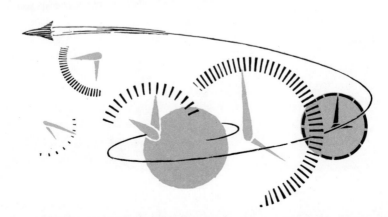

Models of
the Universe

No physicist today disputes the Special Theory of Relativity and few dispute the basic principles of the general theory. It is true that the general theory leaves many important problems unsolved. It is also true that observations and experiments which support the theory are small in number and inconclusive. On the other hand, even if there were no confirmations at all, the general theory would still be enormously attractive because of the great simplifications that it introduces into physics.

Simplifications? This may seem like a strange word to use in reference to a theory employing such advanced mathematics that it was once said that no more than twelve men in the world could understand it (an exaggeration, by the way, even at the time the remark was current). The mathematics of relativity is indeed complicated, but this complexity is balanced by a remarkable simplification in the over-all picture. The reduction of gravity and inertia to the same phenomenon, for example, alone is enough to make general relativity a most efficient way of looking at the world.

Einstein made this point in 1921 when he lectured on relativity at Princeton University. "The possibility," he said, "of explaining the numerical equality of inertia and gravitation by the unity of their nature gives to the General Theory of Relativity, according to my conviction, such a superiority over the conceptions of classical mechanics, that all the difficulties encountered must be considered as small in comparison. . . ."

In addition, relativity theory has what mathematicians like to call "elegance": a kind of artistic grandeur. "Every lover of the beautiful," Lorentz once declared, "must wish it to be true."

In this chapter the fairly solid, agreed-upon aspects of relativity are left behind and the reader is plunged into a misty region of strong controversy: a region where views are no more than tentative suggestions to be accepted or rejected on the basis of evidence that science does not yet possess. What is the universe like as a whole? We know that the earth is the third planet from the sun in a system of nine planets, and that the sun is one of about a hundred billion stars that make up our galaxy. We know that as far as the most powerful telescopes can probe, space is strewn with other galaxies, galaxies that also must be counted by the billions. Does this go on and on forever? Is there an infinity of galaxies? Or does the cosmos have a finite size? (Perhaps we should say, "our cosmos," because if our cosmos is finite, who can say that there are no other finite cosmoses?)

Astronomers try to answer these questions as best they can by constructing what are called models of the universe: imaginary pictures of what the cosmos is like when viewed in its totality. In the early nineteenth century many astronomers assumed that the universe went on and on forever, containing an infinity of suns. Space was Euclidian. Straight lines extended to infinity in all directions. If a spaceship began a journey in any direction and continued in a straight line, it would go on endlessly without ever reaching a boundary. This, of course, is a view that goes back to the ancient Greeks. They liked to say that if a warrior kept throwing his spear farther and farther out into space, he could never reach an end; if such an end were imagined, the warrior could stand there and toss his spear still farther!

There is one important objection to this view. Heinrich Olbers, a German astronomer, pointed out in 1826 that if the number of suns is infinite, and the suns are randomly distributed in space, then a straight line from the earth, in any direction, would eventually intersect a star. This would mean that the entire night sky should be one solid, blinding expanse of starlight. Obviously, it isn't. Some explanation of the dark night sky has to be devised to explain what is now called Olbers' paradox. Most astronomers of the late nineteenth and early twentieth centuries explained it by saying that the number of suns is finite. Our galaxy, they argued, contains all the suns there are. Outside the galaxy? Nothing! (It was not until the mid-twenties of this century that the evidence became overwhelming that there were millions of galaxies at

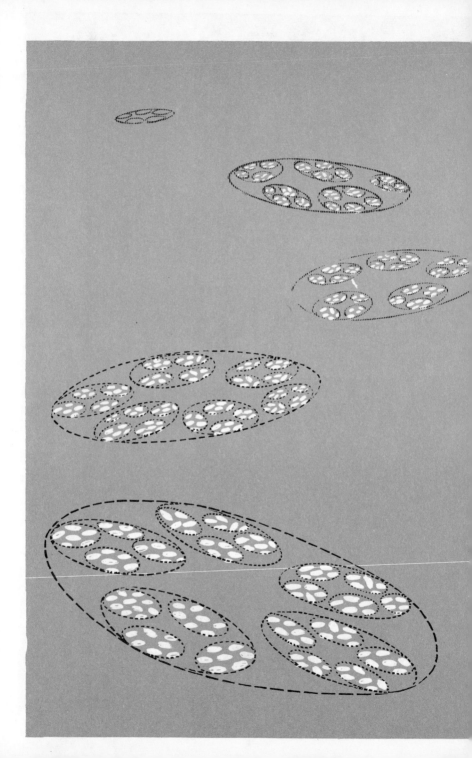

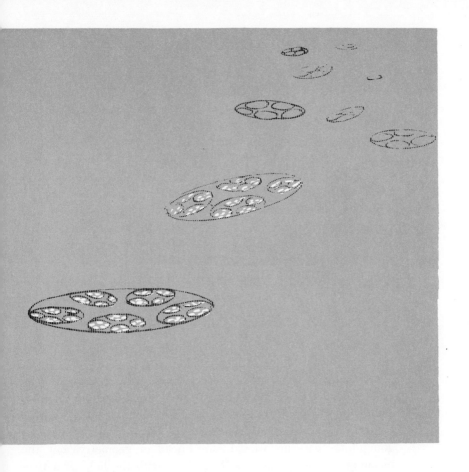

enormous distances from our own.) Other astronomers suggested that the light of distant stars may be blotted out by masses of interstellar fog.

The cleverest explanation of all was advanced by the Swedish mathematician C. V. L. Charlier. Galaxies, he said, are grouped together in clusters. These clusters (he speculated) are grouped into superclusters, the superclusters into super-superclusters, and so on to infinity. At each step to a higher grouping, distances between the groupings grow larger in proportion to the sizes of the groups. If this were true, then the farther a straight line extended from our galaxy, the less the probability that it would encounter another galaxy. On the other hand, the hierarchy of clusters is endless, so it still can be said that the universe contains an infinity of stars. There is nothing wrong with Charlier's explanation of Olbers' paradox, except that there is a simpler explanation. It will be given in a moment.

The first cosmic model based on relativity theory was proposed by Einstein himself in a paper published in 1917. It was an elegant, beautiful model, although Einstein later had to abandon it. On Page 95 it was explained that gravitational fields are the warps or curves produced in the structure of space-time by the presence of large masses of matter. Within every galaxy, therefore, there is a great deal of this twisting and bending of space-time. What about the vast reaches of empty space between the galaxies? One point of view is that the farther space extends, away from the galaxies, the flatter (more Euclidian) space becomes. If the universe were empty of all matter, it would be completely flat, or perhaps it would be meaningless to say that it had any structure at all. In either case, the universe of space-time stretches out to infinity in all directions.

Einstein made an attractive counter-suggestion. Suppose, he said, the amount of matter in the universe is great enough to produce an over-all positive curvature. Space would then curve back on itself in all directions. This cannot be fully understood without going into four-dimensional, non-Euclidian geometry, but the meaning can be grasped easily enough with the help of a two-dimensional model. Imagine a Flatland on which two-dimensional creatures live. They think of it as a Euclidian plane that extends to infinity in all directions. It is true that the suns of Flatland cause various bumps in the plane, but these are localized bumps that do not affect the over-all flatness. There is, however, another possibility that might occur to Flatland astronomers. Perhaps each local bump produces a slight warping of the entire plane so that the total effect of all the suns is to curve the plane until it becomes the surface of a bumpy sphere. Such a plane would still be boundless in the sense that you could move in any direction forever and never come to a boundary. A Flatland warrior would still be unable to find a spot beyond which he could not toss his flat spear. Nevertheless, the surface would be finite. A trip continued long enough in a "straight line" would eventually bring the traveler back to where he started.

Mathematicians say that such a surface is "closed." It is finite

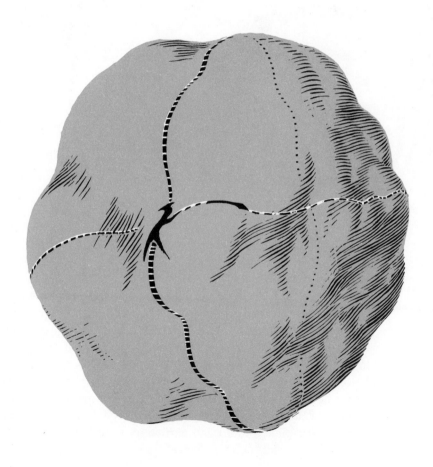

but unbounded. Like infinite Euclidian space, its center is every-where, its circumference nowhere. This "closure," a topological property of the surface, is one that Flatlanders could easily test. One test has already been mentioned: going around the sphere in all directions. Another test would be to paint the surface. If a Flatlander started at one spot and painted larger and larger circles he would eventually paint himself *into* a spot on the oppo-site side of the sphere. If the sphere were large, however, and the Flatlanders confined to a small portion of its surface, they would be unable to make such topological tests.

Einstein suggested that our space is the three-dimensional "surface" of a vast hypersphere (four-dimensional sphere). Time, in his model, remains uncurved: a straight coordinate extending back to an infinite past, forward to an infinite future. If the model is visualized as a four-dimensional space-time structure, it is more like a hypercylinder than a hypersphere. For this reason, the model is usually called the "cylindrical universe." At any instant of time we see space as a kind of three-dimensional cross section of the hypercylinder. Each cross section is the surface of a hypersphere.

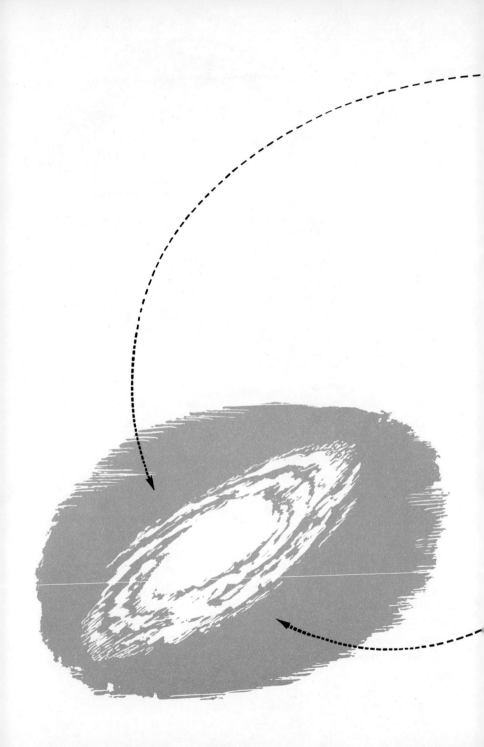

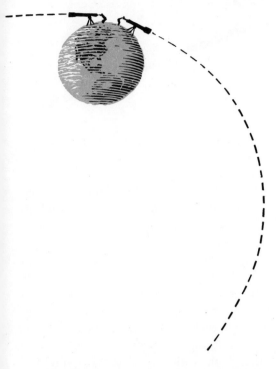

Our galaxy occupies only a minute portion of this surface, so it is not yet possible to perform a topological experiment that will prove its closure. A telescope powerful enough might be focused upon a certain galaxy in one direction, and then upon the *back* of the same galaxy by being pointed in the opposite direction. If there were spaceships that could approach the speed of light, they might be able to circle the cosmos by moving in any direction in the straightest possible line. The cosmos cannot literally be "painted" but essentially the same thing could be done by mapping it, making the spherical maps larger and larger. If the mapper continued long enough, he might find himself passing a point beyond which he would be *inside* the sphere he was mapping. This sphere would grow smaller and smaller as he continued mapping, like the circle that diminishes when a Flatlander paints himself into a spot.

In some ways Einstein's non-Euclidian model is simpler than the classical model in which space is flat. It is simpler in the same sense that a circle may be said to be simpler than a straight line. A straight line stretches off to infinity at both ends, and infinity in mathematics is quite a complicated topic! A circle is comfortably finite. It has no ends; no one need worry about what happens to the line at infinity. Similarly, in Einstein's tidy universe no one need worry about all the loose ends at infinity, about what cosmologists like to call the "boundary conditions." There are no boundary problems in Einstein's cozy universe, because it has no boundaries.

Other cosmic models, all consistent with general relativity, were proposed and debated during the twenties. Some of them have properties even stranger than those of Einstein's cylindrical universe. The Dutch astronomer Willem de Sitter worked out another closed, finite model, but in his model time curves as well as space. The farther one looks through de Sitter's space, the slower clocks seem to be running. If one looks far enough, he arrives at a region where time stops altogether, "like the Mad Hatter's tea party," writes Eddington, "where it is always six o'clock."

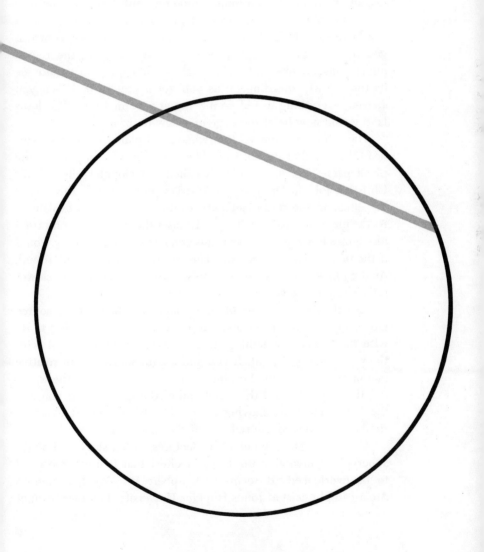

"Not that there is any boundary," explains Bertrand Russell in *The ABC of Relativity*. "The people who live in what our observer takes to be lotus land live just as bustling a life as he does, but get the impression that he is eternally standing still. As a matter of fact, you would never become aware of the lotus land, because it would take an infinite time for light to travel from it to you. You could become aware of places just short of it, but it would remain itself always just beyond your ken." Of course if you traveled to this region in a spaceship, keeping the region under constant observation through a telescope, you would see its time slowly speeding up as you got nearer to it. When you arrived, everything would be moving at a normal rate. The lotus land would now be at the edge of a new horizon.

Have you ever noticed that when an airplane zooms low overhead the sound of its motors suddenly lowers a bit in pitch as the plane passes overhead? This is called the Doppler effect, after Christian Johann Doppler, an Austrian physicist who discovered the effect in the mid-nineteenth century. It is easily explained. As the plane approaches, its speed causes the pulses of sound from its engines to strike your eardrums at a faster rate than they would if the plane were not moving. This raises the pitch of the sound. As the plane moves away, the pulses strike your ears at a slower rate. The pitch lowers.

Exactly the same sort of thing happens when a light source moves rapidly toward or away from you. This has nothing to do with the velocity of light (which is always constant), but with the wavelengths of light. If you and a light source are in relative motion toward one another, the Doppler effect shortens the wavelength of light toward the violet end of the spectrum. If you and the light source are moving apart, the Doppler effect causes a similar shift toward the red end of the spectrum.

George Gamow, in one of his lectures, told a story (no doubt apocryphal) involving the Doppler effect that is much too good to be overlooked. It seems that Robert W. Wood, a famous American physicist at Johns Hopkins University, had been caught

driving through a red light in Baltimore. In his appearance before the judge, Wood gave a brilliant account of the Doppler effect, explaining how his motion toward the red light had shifted the color toward the violet end of the spectrum, causing him to see it as green. The judge was set to waive the fine, but one of Wood's students (whom Wood had recently flunked) happened to be present. He pointed out the speed that would be required in order to shift the traffic light from red to green. The judge dropped the original charge, and fined Wood for speeding.

Doppler thought that the effect he discovered explained the apparent color of distant stars: Reddish stars would be moving away from the earth, bluish stars moving toward the earth. This turned out not to be the case (the colors have other causes), but during the 1920's it was discovered that light from distant galaxies shows a distinct shift toward the red that cannot be accounted for adequately except by assuming that the galaxies are moving away from the earth. Moreover, the shift increases, on the average, in the same proportion as the distance of the galaxy from the earth. If galaxy A is twice as far away as galaxy B, the red shift of A tends to be twice the red shift of B. According to the English astronomer Fred Hoyle, the red shift of the Hydra cluster of galaxies shows the cluster to be moving away from the earth at the stupendous speed of about 38,000 miles per second!

Various attempts have been made to account for this red shift in some other way than by assuming it to be a Doppler effect. One of them, the "tired light" theory, says simply that the longer light travels the slower it vibrates. (This is a perfect example of an *ad hoc* hypothesis, because there is no other evidence to support it.) Another explanation is that the passage of light through cosmic dust causes the shift. De Sitter's model explains the shift neatly in terms of a curving time. But the simplest explanation, the one that fits best with other known facts, is that the red shift does indicate an actual motion of galaxies. A new series of "expanding universe" models were soon developed on this assumption.

It is important to understand that this expansion does not mean that the galaxies themselves are expanding, or even (it now appears) that spaces between the galaxies in a galactic cluster are expanding. The expansion seems to involve the spaces between the clusters. Imagine a huge lump of dough in which hundreds of raisins are embedded in a random way. Each raisin represents a cluster of galaxies. If the dough is baked so that it expands uniformly in all directions, the raisins themselves remain the same size. It is the space between the raisins that grows larger. No one raisin can be called the center of this expansion.

From the viewpoint of any individual raisin, all the other raisins seem to be moving away from it. The more distant the raisin, the faster it seems to recede.

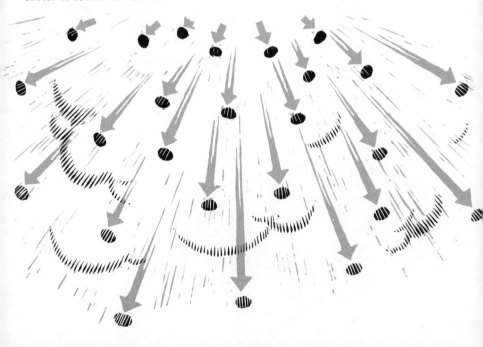

Einstein's model of the universe is static. This, of course, is because he developed it before astronomers decided the universe was expanding. In order to prevent gravitational forces from pulling his cosmos together and collapsing it, he had to suppose that there is another force (he called it the "cosmological constant") which acts as a repelling influence and keeps the stars apart. Later calculations showed that Einstein's model is unstable, like a thin dime balanced on edge. The slightest shove would make it fall heads or tails, heads for an expanding, tails for a collapsing universe. The discovery of the red shift ruled out the contracting universe, so cosmologists turned their attention toward expanding models.

All sorts of expanding models were constructed. The Russian Alexander Friedmann and the Belgian Abbé George Lemaître worked out the two most famous models. Some of these models assume a closed space (positive curvature), some an open space (negative curvature), some leave open the question of whether space is open or closed. Eddington devised a model and wrote a very readable book about it, *The Expanding Universe*. His model is essentially the same as Einstein's, closed like the surface of a vast four-dimensional balloon and expanding uniformly in all three of its spatial dimensions. Today, astronomers doubt that space closes on itself. The density of matter in space seems to be insufficient to account for such an over-all positive curvature. Astronomers prefer the open or infinite universe of over-all negative curvature, like the surface of a saddle.

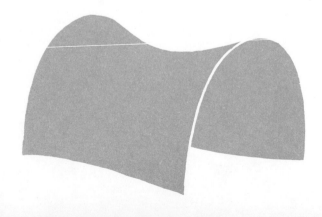

FROM:

The New York Times Book Review

Vol. LXVIII · No. 1 PART 1

© 1963 by The New York Times Company

APRIL 7 1963

RELATIVITY FOR THE MILLION. Martin Gardner. (Macmillan. $6.95.) To the many popular books on relativity, Martin Gardner has added another, a completely successful one, a very model of what such a book should be. Characterized by wit and insight, it is an admirable exposition of subject that carries on every page the ring of authenticity.

No previous book on the subject has been illustrated so elaborately. Anthony Ravielli, a specialist in scientific and mathematical drawing, has produced a set of lively and informative illustrations that at once set this book apart from all predecessors.

Like every book on relativity, this one derives to a considerable extent from a general exposition written by Albert Einstein himself. Mr. Gardner departs from traditional presentations by introducing some of the new experimental confirmations of the theory, the new approaches to certain major problems, and, finally, the new cosmological models. He manages to convey the "elegance" and "artistic grandeur" of relativity. Readers will agree with H. A. Lorentz when he said that "every lover of the beautiful must wish [the theory] to be true."

POPULAR SCIENCE LIVING LIBRARY
355 Lexington Avenue, New York 17, N. Y.

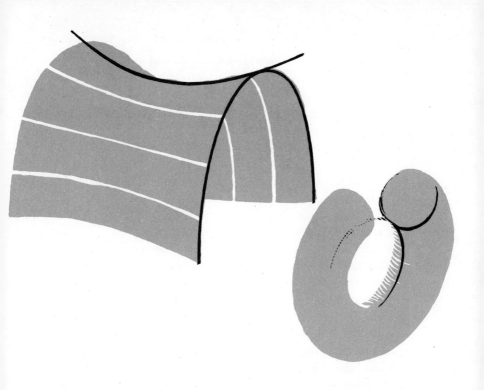

The reader must not suppose that because the surface of a sphere has positive curvature, the *inside* of a sphere's surface has negative curvature. The sphere's surface curvature is positive, whether viewed from one side or the other. The negative curvature of the saddle surface arises from the fact that at any point the surface is curving two different ways. It is concave if you run your hand over it from back to front, convex if you run your hand from side to side. One curvature is expressed by a positive number, the other by a negative number. The two numbers are multiplied to obtain the curvature of the surface at a given point. If at all points this number is negative, as it is sure to be if at all points the surface is curving two different ways, the surface is said to have negative curvature. The surface surrounding the hole of a torus (doughnut) is another familiar example of a surface with negative curvature. Such surfaces are, of course, only crude models of negatively curved three-dimensional space.

Perhaps more powerful telescopes will settle the question of whether the universe has positive, negative, or zero curvature. A telescope can see galaxies only within a certain spherical volume. If the galaxies are randomly distributed, and if space is Euclidian (zero curvature), the number of galaxies within such a sphere should always be proportional to the cube of the sphere's radius. In other words, if a telescope were built that could see twice as far into space as any previous telescope, the number of visible galaxies should jump from n to $8n$. If the jump were less than this it would indicate a positive curving of the universe; if more than this, a negative curving.

One might think it would be the other way around, but consider the case of two-dimensional surfaces of positive and negative curvatures. Suppose a circle is cut from a flat sheet of rubber. On it are glued raisins at distances of a quarter-inch apart. To be formed into the surface of a sphere the rubber must be *compressed* and many raisins brought closer together. In other words, if the raisins are to remain a quarter-inch apart on the spherical surface, *fewer* raisins will be needed. The reverse is true if the rubber is distorted into a saddle surface. This *stretches* the rubber and moves the raisins farther apart. To keep them a quarter-inch apart on the saddle surface, *more* raisins are needed. The moral of all this is, so runs a stale mathematical joke, that when you buy a bottle of beer, be sure to tell the clerk you want a bottle containing space that is curved negatively, not positively!

The expanding-universe models made it unnecessary to retain Einstein's cosmological constant, the hypothetical force that keeps the stars from moving together. (Einstein later considered this concept of a cosmological constant the greatest mistake he ever made.) The new models also cleared up immediately the problem of Olbers' paradox about the brightness of the night sky. Einstein's static model had been of little help on this score. True, it has only a finite number of suns, but because of the closed character of its space, light from these suns is trapped into going round and round the universe forever, twisting this way and that as it is bent by local distortions of space-time. This would light up the

night sky as much as an infinity of suns unless one assumes that the cosmos is so young that light has been able to make only a limited number of round trips.

The notion of an expanding universe eliminates the paradox very simply. If the distant galaxies are moving away from the earth with a speed proportional to their distance, the effect is a dimming of the total amount of light reaching the earth. If a galaxy is far enough away, its speed will exceed that of light. Its light will never reach us at all. Many astronomers today seriously believe that if the universe were not expanding there literally would be no difference between night and day.

The fact that distant galaxies may exceed the speed of light relative to the earth seems to violate the dictum that no material body can go faster than light. But as we saw in Chapter 4, this dictum holds only for conditions that meet the requirements of the special theory. In the general theory, it must be rephrased as the dictum that no signals can be transmitted faster than light. Still, there is considerable controversy over whether distant galaxies actually can pass through the light barrier, so to speak, and vanish forever from man's ability to see them even if he had the most powerful telescopes imaginable. Some experts think the speed of light *is* a limit here, so that the most distant galaxies would simply grow dimmer and dimmer without ever becoming totally invisible, provided man had sufficiently sensitive instruments for detecting them.

Old galaxies, someone was the first to say, never die. They just fade away. It is important to understand, however, that no galaxy actually vanishes in the sense that its matter disappears from the universe. It merely reaches a speed that makes it impossible, or almost impossible, for the earth's telescopes to detect it. The vanishing galaxy continues to be visible, of course, from all galaxies that surround it at closer range. For each galaxy there is an "optical horizon," a spherical boundary, beyond which its telescopes cannot penetrate. These spherical horizons are not the same for any two galaxies. Astronomers calculate that the point at which galaxies may be vanishing over *our* "rim" is about twice as far away as any present optical telescope can reach. If this assumption is correct, about one-eighth of all the galaxies that will ever be visible are now being seen.

If the universe is expanding (it does not matter whether space be flat, open, or closed), then a tantalizing question arises. What was the universe like if one goes back as far as he can in time? There are two essentially different ways to answer this, each the cornerstone for a popular contemporary model of the universe. Both models will be examined in the next chapter.

10

Big Bang
or Steady
State?

PICTURE in your mind an expanding cosmos, then run the scene backward, like a motion picture in reverse. It is apparent that there must have been a moment, in what Shakespeare once called the "dark backward and abysm of time," when an enormous amount of matter was concentrated in a very small space. Perhaps a great primeval explosion, many billions of years ago, started the whole process. This is the Big Bang concept, first advocated by Lemaître (see page 148) and now finding its most able champion in George Gamow, the Russian-born physicist whose name has already appeared several times in this book.

Gamow has written a persuasive book, *The Creation of the Universe,* in defense of his theory. Lemaitre thought the Big Bang took place about 5 billion years ago, but estimates of the age of the universe have also been expanding in recent years. It now appears that 20 to 25 billion is a much better guess. At any rate, according to Gamow there was a time when all the matter in the universe was concentrated in one incredibly dense, uniform glob of concentrated matter called Ylem (pronounced "eelem"; it is an old Greek word for primordial matter). How did the Ylem get there? Gamow thinks it previously may have been spread out through the space of a *collapsing* universe. This period of the Big Squeeze is obviously a period about which nothing can be learned. Like Lemaître's model, Gamow's model really begins with a Bang. This is sometimes called the "moment of creation"; not in the sense of making something out of nothing, Gamow has explained, but in the sense of making a shape out of something previously shapeless. If belief in a creation out of nothing is preferred, *this* is as good a point as any, in Gamow's theory, to pick for it.

Just before the Big Bang, the temperature and pressure of the Ylem was incredibly high. Then came the monstrous, unimaginable explosion. Gamow's book will supply all the details of what may have happened after that. Eventually the stars congealed from the expanding dust and gas. The present expansion of the universe is the continuation of the motion imparted to matter by the initial explosion. Gamow believes that the motion will never stop.

The chief rival at the moment to Gamow's Big Bang is the Steady State universe proposed in 1948 by three Cambridge University scientists: Hermann Bondi, Thomas Gold, and Fred Hoyle. The most persuasive defense of *this* theory is Hoyle's popular book, *The Nature of the Universe*. Like Gamow's theory, the Steady State theory accepts the expansion of the universe and assumes space to be open and infinite rather than closed as in Eddington's model. Unlike Gamow's theory it does not start with a Bang. In fact, it does not start at all. Not by accident does the title of Hoyle's book differ from Gamow's only by the change of one word. Hoyle's cosmos has no moment of "creation"; or rather it has, as we shall see, an infinity of small creations. As Hoyle expresses it: "Every cluster of galaxies, every star, every atom had a beginning, but not the Universe itself. The Universe is something more than its parts, a perhaps unexpected conclusion." *

The Steady State universe is always in the running, just the way it is now. Going back a hundred thousand billion years, the same types of evolving galaxies are found in any portion of the cosmos, containing the same types of aging stars, some with the same types of planets whirling around them, and on some of these planets, probably, similar types of life. There may be an infinity of planets on which at this very moment (whatever that may mean) intelligent creatures are sending their first astronauts into space. The cosmos is uniform, in an over-all way, throughout an infinite space and an infinite time. Its expansion is not the aftermath of an explosion. It is due to a basic repulsive force of some sort, the nature of which is still hotly debated. This force is similar to Einstein's abandoned cosmological constant. It pushes the galaxies apart until finally they vanish over the "rim" as they pass through the light barrier. This disappearance is, of course, from the standpoint of an observer in our galaxy. When an observer on the earth sees Galaxy X and its neighbors fade away, observers in Galaxy X see *our* galaxy do the same thing.

* Fred Hoyle, *Frontiers of Astronomy*. New York: New American Library paperback ed., 1957, p. 284.

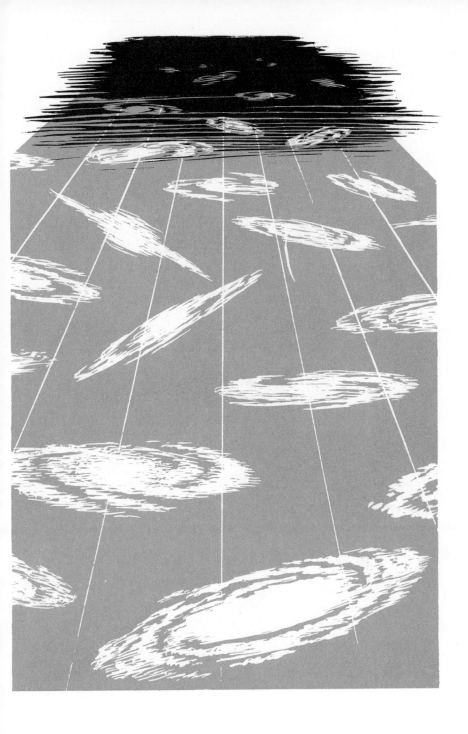

An all-important question remains. If the universe has always been expanding and will keep on expanding forever, why doesn't it thin itself out? Clearly there is no way to maintain the Steady State without assuming that new matter is constantly being created, perhaps in the form of hydrogen, the simplest of the elements, According to Hoyle (it is almost impossible to write about Hoyle's views without indulging in this obvious play on words), if one hydrogen atom per bucketful of space were to come into existence about every 10 million years, it would keep the cosmos steady. Naturally, the rate at which matter forms has to be just such as to balance the thinning-out process.

Where do the hydrogen atoms come from? No one presumes to know. This is the point at which Hoyle's theory begins. If a belief in creation from nothing is maintained, *this* is the point in the Steady State theory where creation takes place, or rather, where it constantly takes place.

Both of these rival theories, the Big Bang and the Steady State, can be adjusted to fit all the known facts about the cosmos (or, more accurately, what are *thought at the moment* to be the known facts), as well as all the principles of relativity. At present the two theories are running about neck and neck. Every year some new observations support the Big Bang theory and cast doubt on the Steady State, but they are balanced by new observations that support the Steady State and cast doubt on the Big Bang. If you should read an article or book by a champion of either theory you may find the author writing as if all the evidence is on his side and very little on the side of his stubborn, out-of-date opponents. You don't have to believe him. Where experts disagree it is prudent not to take sides unless you have a strong emotional preference for one theory over the other. Gamow has written frankly about his emotional preference for the Big Bang, Hoyle has been equally frank about his emotional preference for a Steady State. (So far as I know, the psychoanalysts haven't yet explained both theories on the basis of the neuroses of the men who advocate them, but you can be sure they'll get around to it eventually.) Aside from an emotional bias, it is well to suspend judgment until the astronomers are able to bring in enough evidence to tilt the scales one way or another.

There are many other cosmic models, some advanced seriously, some in jest. There are models in which space twists back on itself like a Moebius strip (a one-sided surface formed by giving a strip of paper a half-twist and joining the ends). If you travel once around such a universe you find yourself back where you started, only everything is reversed as in a mirror. Of course you can go around once more and straighten everything out. There are oscillating models that alternate Big Bangs with periods of expansion and contraction. The cycle keeps repeating forever, like the eternal reoccurrence doctrines of certain philosophers and Eastern religions. (Curiously, Edgar Allan Poe defended an oscillating universe, now in its collapsing stage, in a strange cosmological work called *Eureka,* by which he set great store.) The "kinematic relativity" model of the Oxford University astronomer Edward A. Milne is perhaps the most bizarre of all. It introduces two essentially different kinds of time. In terms of one time the universe is infinite in age and size, not expanding at all. In terms of the other time it is finite in size and has been expanding only since a moment of creation. It is a matter of convenience which kind of time is taken as basic.

The English mathematician Edmund Whittaker once proposed (as a joke) a diminishing universe theory in which a finite cosmos not only contracts, but as it does so, matter continually vanishes back into wherever it comes from in Hoyle's theory. The world eventually fades completely away, not with a Bang but a Whimper. "This would have the recommendation," Whittaker writes, "of supplying a very simple picture of the final destiny of the universe." Of course such a theory would have to explain why we see a galactic red shift instead of a violet one, but this is not hard to account for. All we have to do is borrow one of de Sitter's devices and assume that time is getting faster. (As a friend, Sidney Margulies, has pointed out, this might explain why, as one grows older, the years seem to slip by like months. They *are* slipping by like months!) Light that reaches the earth from a distant galaxy would then be light from the galaxy as it appeared millions of years ago when its light vibrated more slowly. This could produce a red shift large enough to more than balance the Doppler shift to the violet. Of course, the farther away the galaxy, the older and redder it would appear.

The fact that a diminishing model can be constructed shows how flexible are the equations of relativity. They can be fitted to scores of different cosmic models, all of which account fairly well for everything that can at present be observed. It is interesting to find the English philosopher Francis Bacon, writing in his *Novum Organum* in 1620: "Many hypotheses with regard to the heavens can be formed, differing in themselves, and yet sufficiently according with the phenomena." Modern cosmology is unchanged in this respect, though the amount of phenomena observed is much greater; therefore, there are good grounds for supposing that modern models are closer to the truth than the old. Of course the fashionable cosmic models of a hundred years from now, based on astronomical data not known at the moment, may be wildly unlike any model now taken seriously.

It is with this humbling thought in mind that so many writers on modern cosmology, from Eddington to Sciama, have quoted from Book 8 of John Milton's *Paradise Lost*. The angel Raphael is speaking to Adam and Eve. Note how the relativity of the earth's motion is assumed.

> To ask or search I blame thee not; for Heaven
> Is as the Book of God before thee set,
> Wherein to read his wondrous works, and learn
> His seasons, hours, or days, or months, or years.
> This to attain, whether Heaven move or Earth
> Imports not, if thou reckon right; the rest
> From Man or Angel the great Architect
> Did wisely to conceal, and not divulge
> His secrets, to be scanned, by them who ought
> Rather admire. Or, if they list to try
> Conjecture, he his fabric of the Heavens
> Hath left to their disputes—perhaps to move
> His laughter at their quaint opinions wide
> Hereafter, when they come to model Heaven,
> And calculate the stars.

There is an amusing short tale by the Irish writer Lord Dunsany (in his book *The Man Who Ate the Phoenix*) in which Atlas explains to Dunsany what happened on the day when science made it no longer possible for mortals to believe in the old Greek model of the universe. Atlas admits that he had found his task rather dull and unpleasant. He was cold, because he had the earth's South Pole on the back of his neck, and his hands were always wet from the two oceans. But he remained at his task as long as people believed in him.

Then the world, Atlas says sadly, began to get "too scientific." He decided he was no longer needed. So he just put down the world and walked away.

"Yes," Atlas says. "Not without reflection, not without considerable reflection. But when I did it, I must say I was profoundly astonished; utterly astonished at what happened."

"And what did happen?"

"Simply nothing. Simply nothing at all."

In this book I have tried to tell the story of what happened on a more recent occasion when Newton's God of Absolute Motion, after a couple of prods by Einstein, put down the earth and walked away. Nothing much happened to the earth, at least not for a while. It continued to rotate on its axis, bulge at its equator, whirl around the sun. But something did happen to physics. Its power to explain, its power to predict, above all its power to alter the face of the earth for good or evil, became greater than it had ever been before.

Glossary

The purpose of this glossary is to give simple, intuitively clear definitions, within the limits of an elementary book, rather than technically precise definitions. A complete explanation of "curvature," for example, would be out of the question; it would require several pages. The reader who wishes more detailed, technical definitions should refer to an appropriate encyclopedia or textbook.

Absolute Motion: Motion relative to a fixed ether, or some equally universal, preferred frame of reference.

Acceleration: A change in the speed, direction, or both, of a moving object.

Ad hoc **Hypothesis:** A theory concocted to explain one set of observations, but completely unsupported by other observations.

Antimatter: Matter composed of antiparticles.

Antiparticle: An elementary particle that is the same as an ordinary particle, except that its charge and/or magnetic moment is reversed. For charged particles, both are reversed. For neutral particles, which have no charge, the distinction is based on a reversal of the magnetic moment.

Big Bang Theory: The theory that the universe had its origin in a monstrous primeval explosion of Ylem.

c: Conventional symbol for the velocity of light: about 186,000 miles (300,-000 kilometers) per second.

Centrifugal Force: The inertial force that impels an object, or parts of an object, outward from a center of rotation.

Clock Paradox: The startling assertion of relativity theory that two synchronized clocks can be separated and brought together again in such a way that the clocks will no longer be synchronized, even though both kept perfect time.

Conservation of Mass-Energy: The theory that the total amount of mass-energy in the universe can neither be increased nor diminished.

Coordinate: One of a set of numbers used for locating a point. On a line, one coordinate is needed; on a plane, two coordinates; in space, three coordinates; in space-time, four coordinates.

Cosmos: The entire space-time universe. Sometimes called the metagalaxy.

Curvature: Deviation from "straight" or "flat" of a line, surface, or space.

Cylindrical Universe: Albert Einstein's first model of the cosmos. Its three space coordinates curve positively; its time coordinate is straight.

Doppler Effect: Changes in the apparent wavelength of sound or electromagnetic radiation, caused by the relative motion of an observer to or away from the source of the wave.

Electromagnetic Spectrum: The entire range of electromagnetic radiation, from waves of extremely large to waves of extremely small length.

Electromagnetic Wave: A radiation produced by the oscillation of an electric charge. It travels through empty space with a constant speed relative to a uniformly moving observer, regardless of the speed of its source or the speed of the observer.

Elliptic Geometry: A non-Euclidian geometry in which, on a plane, no line can be drawn through a point outside a line, parallel to that line.

Energy: The capacity to perform work.

Ether: A substance believed by nineteenth-century physics to permeate all space, serving as the medium for the propagation of electromagnetic radiation.

Ether Wind: A movement of the ether past an object traveling through it.

Euclidian Geometry: A geometry based on the postulates of Euclid.

Euclidian Space: A space with zero curvature.

Free Fall: The movement of an object in space, under the influence of no forces other than gravity.

Fourth Dimension: Any fourth coordinate in a system of coordinates. In relativity theory, time is conventionally regarded as the fourth dimension.

Frame of Reference: A coordinate system assumed to be fixed, and relative to which measurements of time, motion, length, mass, and so on, are made.

g: An acceleration (produced by gravity or inertia) of 32 feet per second per second.

Galaxy: A community of billions of stars, often lens-shaped, moving as a unit through space.

Galilean System: See inertial frame.

General Theory of Relativity: Einstein's second theory of relativity, generalizing his special theory to include accelerated motion, gravity, and inertia.

Geodesic: The "straightest" line between two points on a given surface or in a given space or space-time; the line connecting two points that has an extreme (longest or shortest) length.

Gravitational Mass: The mass of an object viewed as the generator of a gravitational field or as in response to such a field. On earth it is measured as the object's weight.

Gravity: According to Newton, a force of attraction between any two bodies, varying directly with the product of their masses and inversely with the square of the distance between them. According to Einstein, the tendency of material bodies, free from the influence of other forces, to move through space-time along geodesics.

Hyperbolic Geometry: A non-Euclidian geometry in which, on a plane, an infinite number of lines can be drawn through a point outside a line and parallel to that line.

Hypersphere: A four-dimensional sphere.

Inertia: The tendency of matter to remain at rest relative to an inertial frame or to move with uniform velocity in a straight line unless acted upon by an outside force.

Inertial Frame: A coordinate system moving uniformly through space relative to all other inertial frames. Same as inertial system or Galilean system.

Inertial Mass: The mass of an object viewed as its resistance to an alteration of its motion. It is measured by the force required to increase the acceleration of the object by a given amount.

Inertial System: See inertial frame.

Kennedy-Thorndike experiment: A later repetition of the Michelson-Morley experiment, using apparatus with arms of different length.

Light: The visible portion of the electromagnetic spectrum.

Lorentz-Fitzgerald Contraction: The relativistic contraction of an object in the direction in which it is moving.

Mach's Principle: The theory that inertia arises from the accelerated motion of an object relative to all the matter in the cosmos.

Mass: Roughly, the amount of matter in an object.

Michelson-Morley Experiment: A famous experiment demonstrating the absence of an ether wind as the earth moves through space.

Negative Acceleration: A decrease in velocity.

Negative Mass: Hypothetical property of an object which, if it existed, would cause the object to move in a direction opposite to the direction of a force acting upon it.

Non-Euclidian Geometry: A geometry in which one or more of Euclid's postulates are replaced by others.

Olber's Paradox: The surprising calculation that the entire sky should at all times be brighter than the sun, provided galaxies are uniformly distributed in space, and the universe is infinite in time and space, and not expanding.

Optical Horizon: The spherical limit (in an expanding universe) that can be reached by telescopes, no matter how powerful, because beyond that limit galaxies would be moving away from the observer with a speed equal to or greater than that of light.

Oscillating Universe: A universe that alternately expands and contracts.

Postulate: An assumption, made without proof, that forms part of the groundwork of a logical system. Sometimes called an axiom.

Principle of equivalence: The assertion, basic to the General Theory of Relativity, that gravity and inertia are two different ways of viewing essentially the same phenomena.

Red Shift: A shift toward the red in the wavelength of light. Such a shift may be due to: 1. Relative motion of the source away from the observer; 2. Influence of a stronger gravitational field; 3. Origin of the light in an earlier period, on the assumption that time is getting faster.

Rest Mass: The mass of an object at rest relative to the observer.

Signal: Any cause-and-effect chain of events passing from one body to another.

Space-Time: The four-dimensional coordinate system of relativity.

Space-Time Interval: The distance between two events, measured in space-time.

Space-Time Structure: The geometrical structure of space-time.

Special Theory of Relativity: Einstein's first theory of relativity, concerned only with observers in inertial frames.

Steady State Theory: The theory that the cosmos has no beginning or end in time, but maintains a large-scale "steady state" as new matter is constantly created to replace matter moving outward with the expansion of the universe.

Thought experiment: An experiment that can be performed only in the mind, not in actual practice.

Topology: Roughly, the study of properties that are unchanged when a figure undergoes continuous deformation.

Twin Paradox: The principle of the clock paradox applied to a hypothetical pair of twins. One twin goes on a space voyage at a high velocity; relative to the earth's inertial frame his aging process is slowed down, and he returns to earth younger than his stay-at-home brother.

Unified Field Theory: A theory, as yet unsatisfactorily developed, in which gravity and electromagnetism are unified by a common set of equations.

Wavelength: The distance, measured in the direction a wave is moving, from one point on the wave to the next point that is, at the moment, in the same phase.

World Line: The path of a moving object, charted on a four-dimensional space-time coordinate system.

Ylem: The primordial substance that supposedly exploded billions of years ago, forming the present expanding universe.

Zero g: Zero gravity, the condition of weightlessness in space far removed from matter or in a spaceship in a state of free fall.

Chronology

1879 Albert Einstein is born (March 14) at Ulm, Germany.

1881 Albert Michelson makes his first attempt to detect the ether wind.

1887 The Michelson-Morley experiment fails to find an ether wind.

1893 H. A. Lorentz publishes his first contraction theory to explain the Michelson-Morley test.

1905 Einstein publishes his Special Theory of Relativity.

1908 Roland von Eötvös completes his extraordinarily precise tests proving that inertial mass is proportional to gravitational mass.

Hermann Minkowski gives his famous lecture on space and time as mere "shadows" of a fundamental space-time.

1911 Einstein proposes that the bending of starlight by gravity be tested during a total eclipse of the sun.

1916 Einstein completes his work on the General Theory of Relativity.

1917 Einstein describes his model of a "cylindrical universe." The beginning of modern cosmology.

1919 Arthur Stanley Eddington leads an expedition to Africa to observe a solar eclipse; measurements confirm Einstein's prediction of the effect of gravity on starlight.

1932 The Kennedy-Thorndike experiment repeats the Michelson-Morley test in such a way that it falsifies the original Lorentz contraction theory.

1942 Enrico Fermi and his associates achieve the first sustained nuclear chain reaction. Mass is turned into energy in accordance with Einstein's formula. The atomic age begins.

1955 Death of Einstein (April 18) at Princeton, New Jersey.

1958 Rudolf Mössbauer discovers the "Mössbauer effect," leading quickly to experiments confirming Einstein's prediction that time is slowed down by gravity.

Suggestions for Further Reading

Popular Books on Relativity

Barnett, Lincoln, *The Universe and Dr. Einstein*. New York: William Morrow & Co., Inc., 1948. Revised edition, New York: New American Library of World Literature, Inc. ("Mentor Books," paperback), 1952. By a former science writer for *Life* magazine; foreword by Albert Einstein.

Borel, Emile, *Space and Time*. London and Glasgow: Blackie and Son, Ltd., 1926. New York: Dover Publications, Inc. (paperback), 1960. A popular book, first published in 1922, by a prominent French mathematician and writer.

Coleman, James A., *Relativity for the Layman*. New York: The Macmillan Company, 1959. New York: New American Library of World Literature, Inc. ("Mentor Books"), 1958. A recent introduction by the chairman of the physics department, American International College, Springfield, Massachusetts.

Durell, Clement V., *Readable Relativity*. London: G. Bell and Sons. Ltd., 1926. New York: Harper and Brothers ("Harper Torchbook," paperback), 1960. An excellent book by a Cambridge University mathematician.

Eddington, Sir Arthur S., *Space, Time and Gravitation*. Cambridge: The University Press, 1920. New York: Harper and Brothers ("Harper Torchbook"), 1961. Unrevised, but still a stimulating survey by the distinguished English astronomer.

Einstein, Albert and Infeld, Leopold, *The Evolution of Physics*. New York: Simon and Schuster, 1938. An excellent account of the history of modern physics with emphasis on relativity and quantum theory.

Frank, Philipp, *Relativity, A Richer Truth*. Boston: Beacon Press, 1950. An enlightening philosophical discussion by a leading German philosopher of science. Foreword by Albert Einstein.

Gamow, George, *Gravity*. Garden City, L. I.: Doubleday & Company, Inc.

("Anchor Books," paperback), 1962. An up-to-date treatise by the well-known professor of physics at the University of Colorado. Written with his usual clarity and humor.

Infeld, Leopold, *Albert Einstein.* New York: Charles Scribner's Sons ("Scribner Library," paperback), 1950. An introduction to relativity (not a biography) by Einstein's friend and collaborator, a leading Polish physicist.

Jaffe, Bernard, *Michelson and the Speed of Light.* Garden City, L. I.: Doubleday & Company, Inc. ("Anchor Books"), 1960. A biography of Michelson, including a full account of the famous Michelson-Morley test.

Landau, L. D. and Rumer, G. S., *What is Relativity?* New York: Basic Books, Inc., 1960. A very elementary presentation of the special theory only, but written with skill and humor by two leading Russian physicists.

Lieber, Lillian, *The Einstein Theory of Relativity.* New York, Toronto: Farrar, Straus & Cudahy, Inc., 1945. Very elementary, but delightfully presented, with amusing illustrations by Hugh Lieber.

Reichenbach, Hans, *From Copernicus to Einstein.* New York: Philosophical Library, Inc., 1942. Stresses the basic ideas of relativity in relation to the philosophy of science.

Russell, Bertrand, *The ABC of Relativity.* New York, London: Harper & Brothers, 1925. Revised edition, New York: New American Library of World Literature, Inc. ("Mentor Books"), 1959. An excellent book, written by England's most distinguished living philosopher.

Semi-popular Books on Relativity

D'Abro, A., *The Evolution of Scientific Thought from Newton to Einstein.* New York: Boni & Liveright, Inc., 1927. New York: Dover Publications, Inc. (paperback), 1950. Contains a superb exposition of relativity theory.

Einstein, Albert, *Relativity: The Special and General Theory.* New York: Holt, Rinehart & Winston, Inc., 1920. New York: Crown Publishers, Inc. (paperback), 1961. Einstein's famous and only non-technical account of relativity.

Einstein, Albert, *Sidelights on Relativity.* New York: E. P. Dutton & Co., Inc., 1923. Two important lectures by Einstein: "Ether and Relativity" and "Geometry and Experience."

Jammer, Max, *Concepts of Space.* Cambridge: Harvard University Press, 1954. New York: Harper and Brothers ("Harper Torchbooks"), 1960. A history of theories of space, with an important foreword by Einstein.

Reichenbach, Hans, *The Philosophy of Space and Time.* New York: Dover Publications, 1958. A translation from the German of the best book ever written on relativity as related to the philosophy of science.

Schilpp, Paul A. (ed.), *Albert Einstein: Philosopher-Scientist.* First edition, Evanston, Illinois: Library of Living Philosophers, 1949. Second edition, New York: Tudor Publishing Co., 1951. Critical essays on Einstein's work, Einstein's replies, bibliography of Einstein's writings, and his valuable "Autobiographical Notes."

Whittaker, Sir Edmund, *A History of the Theories of Aether and Electricity, 1900–1926.* New York: Philosophical Library, 1954. Harper and Brothers ("Harper Torchbooks," 1960.) An important historical account, marred by a curious attempt to minimize the scope of Einstein's contributions.

Technical Books on Relativity

Bergmann, P. G., *Introduction to the Theory of Relativity.* New York: Prentice-Hall, Inc., 1942. One of the best of modern textbooks, by a German-born professor of physics at Syracuse University.

Eddington, Sir Arthur S., *The Mathematical Theory of Relativity.* Cambridge: The University Press, 1923. Cambridge: The University Press (paperback), 1960. An excellent reference work.

Einstein, Albert and others, *The Principle of Relativity.* Calcutta: The University of Calcutta, 1920. New York: Dover Publications, (paperback), 1956(?). Historic papers by Einstein, Lorentz, Minkowski and Weyl.

Einstein, Albert, *The Meaning of Relativity.* Princeton: Princeton University Press, 1956. Fifth edition of four lectures given by Einstein at Princeton University in 1921.

McCrea, W. H., *Relativity Physics.* First edition, London: Methuen & Co., Ltd., 1935. Fourth edition, 1954. A compact handbook by a professor of mathematics at the University of London.

Milne, E. A., *Relativity, Gravity, and World Structure.* New York: Oxford University Press, 1935. An account of the author's "kinematic relativity," based on Einstein's special theory but in sharp conflict with the general theory.

Møller, Christian, *The Theory of Relativity.* Oxford: The Clarendon Press, 1935. An excellent modern textbook by a professor of physics at the University of Copenhagen.

Pauli, Wolfgang, *Theory of Relativity.* New York: Pergamon Press, 1958. Translation of a justly famous article written for a German encyclopedia in 1921, when the author, a world-renowned physicist, was 21. Updated with notes by the author.

Rainich, George, *Mathematics of Relativity.* New York: John Wiley & Sons, Inc., 1950. A standard reference by a leading Russian-born physicist, who is professor emeritus at the University of Michigan.

Schrödinger, Erwin, *Space-Time Structure.* Cambridge: The University Press, 1950. A standard work by the great German physicist.

Synge, John Lighton, *Relativity: the Special Theory. Relativity: the General Theory*. New York: Interscience Publishers, Inc., Vol. 1, 1956, Vol. 2, 1960. By a world-famous Irish physicist. Volume 2 contains an extensive, up-to-date bibliography of 63 pages.

Tolman, Richard C. *Relativity, Thermodynamics and Cosmology*. New York: Oxford University Press, 1934. A splendid survey by a professor of physics and chemistry at the California Institute of Technology. Contains a very clear discussion of the mathematics of the clock paradox.

Weyl, Hermann, *Space, Time and Matter*. London: Methuen & Co., Ltd., 1922. Original contributions to relativity by one of the greatest of modern mathematicians.

Semi-popular Articles on Relativity

Cohen, I. Bernard, "An Interview with Einstein," *Scientific American* (July, 1955). An important interview, two weeks before Albert Einstein's death, by a distinguished professor of the history of science, Harvard University.

De Benedetti, Sergio, The Mössbauer Effect," *Scientific American* (March, 1960). An account, by an Italian-born professor of physics at the Carnegie Institute of Technology, of a new "atomic clock" that is involved in many recent confirmations of general relativity.

Dicke, R. H., "The Eötvös Experiment," *Scientific American* (December, 1961). Details on a historic experiment confirming the proportionality of inertial and gravitational mass, and its latest refinements.
    "New Thinking about Gravitation," *The New Scientist* (December 28, 1961). The author is a particle physicist at Princeton University.

Grünbaum, Adolf, "Logical and Philosophical Foundations of the Special Theory of Relativity," in A. Danto and S. Morgenbesser, eds., *Philosophy of Science*. New York: Meridian Press (paperback), 1960. The author is a well-known philosopher of science at the University of Pittsburgh.

Reichenbach, Hans, "The Present State of the Discussion of Relativity," in *Modern Philosophy of Science*. London: Routledge and Kegan, 1959. Rich source of historical data and insights, first published in 1921.

Rothman, Milton A., "Things that Go Faster than Light," *Scientific American* (July, 1960). The author is a research physicist on Project Matterhorn, investigating nuclear fusion power, at Princeton University.

Teller, Edward, "The Geometry of Space and Time," *The Mathematics Teacher* (November, 1961). Stimulating, amusing lecture by a world famous nuclear physicist, at the opening session of the IBM Junior Science Symposium, 1960.

Popular Books on Modern Cosmology

Bondi, Hermann, *The Universe at Large*. Garden City, L. I.: Doubleday &

Company, Inc. ("Anchor Books"), 1960. Introduction to modern cosmology by one of the co-authors of the Steady State theory.

Eddington, Sir Arthur S., *The Expanding Universe*. New York: The Macmillan Company, 1933. Ann Arbor, Michigan: University of Michigan Press ("Ann Arbor Paperbacks"), 1958. A sparkling defense of the author's now-dated model of an expanding cosmos.

Gamow, George, *The Creation of the Universe*. New York: The Viking Press, Inc., 1952; rev. ed., 1961, ("Compass Books," paperback, 1956). The classic popular defense of the Big Bang hypothesis.

Hoyle, Fred, *The Nature of the Universe*. New York: Harper and Brothers, 1950; rev. ed., 1960. New York: New American Library of World Literature, Inc. ("Mentor Books"), 1955. The classic popular defense of the Steady State hypothesis and the first book to bring this theory to the attention of the general public.

Munitz, Milton K. (ed.), *Theories of the Universe*. New York: Free Press of Glencoe, Inc., 1957. Selected readings in the history of cosmology. The author is professor of philosophy at New York University.

––– *Space, Time and Creation*. New York: Free Press of Glencoe, Inc., 1957. An analysis of modern cosmologies. New York: Collier Books (paperback), 1962.

Sciama, Dennis, *The Unity of the Universe*. Garden City, L. I.: Doubleday & Company, Inc., 1959 ("Anchor Books," 1961). A defense of the Steady State theory combined with a new Machian theory of inertia by the author, a leading English cosmologist.

Whitrow, G. J., *The Structure and Evolution of the Universe*. New York; Harper and Brothers ("Harper Torchbook"), 1959. A readable introduction to cosmology by a mathematician at the University of London.

Semi-popular Books on Modern Cosmology

Bondi, Hermann, *Cosmology*. Cambridge: The University Press, 1952 (paperback, 1961). An excellent nontechnical survey of modern cosmology from the Steady State point of view.

Johnson, Martin, *Time, Knowledge, and the Nebulae*. New York: Dover Publications, 1947. A nontechnical exposition of the unorthodox relativity and cosmology of E. A. Milne.

Kapp, Reginald O. *Towards a Unified Cosmology*. New York: Basic Books, Inc., 1960. Free-wheeling speculation by a professor emeritus at the University of Birmingham, England, including the author's theory of gravity.

Index

About the Author

Martin Gardner, as well as editing the Mathematical Games Department of *Scientific American*, is an established author of popular books on science and mathematics, including the *Scientific American Book of Mathematical Puzzles* and *Fads and Fallacies*. He began his writing career as a newspaper reporter, received his B.A. in philosophy at the University of Chicago in 1936, and worked as a publicity writer for the university. During World War II he served as a yeoman on a destroyer escort.

Relativity for the Million reflects Mr. Gardner's long interest in Einstein's theories. "The purpose of this book," he says, "is to explain these ideas in as simple, straightforward, and entertaining a way as possible, without vulgarizing or distorting, and with a minimum of mathematics."

Born in Tulsa, Oklahoma, he now lives with his wife and two sons in Dobbs Ferry, New York.

About the Illustrator

Anthony Ravielli is a full-time artist noted for his lively and accurate scientific and mathematical drawings. One of five children, all of whom chose artistic careers, Mr. Ravielli attended Textile High School in his native New York City. After graduation he studied art at Cooper Union and the Art Students League. He began his professional career as a portrait painter, later turning to illustrating, providing drawings for *Sports Illustrated* and a number of leading advertising agencies.

Mr. Ravielli has both written and illustrated a number of books including the award-winning *Wonders of the Human Body* and *An Adventure in Geometry*. He now lives with his family in Stamford, Connecticut.